MEDIA LITERACY
THINKING CRITICALLY ABOUT
ADVERTISING

Peyton Paxson

WALCH PUBLISHING

User's Guide
to
Walch Reproducible Books

1   2   3   4   5   6   7   8   9   10

ISBN 0-8251-4365-9

Copyright © 2002
J. Weston Walch, Publisher
P.O. Box 658 • Portland, Maine 04104-0658
www.walch.com

Printed in the United States of America

User's Guide
to
Walch Reproducible Books

Purchasers of this book are granted the right to reproduce all pages.

This permission is limited to a single teacher, for classroom use only.

Any questions regarding this policy or requests to purchase further reproduction rights should be addressed to

Permissions Editor
J. Weston Walch, Publisher
321 Valley Street • P.O. Box 658
Portland, Maine 04104-0658

1   2   3   4   5   6   7   8   9   10

ISBN 0-8251-4365-9

Copyright © 2002
J. Weston Walch, Publisher
P.O. Box 658 • Portland, Maine 04104-0658
www.walch.com

Printed in the United States of America

Contents

Contents

Contents

To the Teacher

The Magazine Publishers of America tell us:

> Today's teenagers reflect a diverse and complicated cross-section of attitudes, ethnicities, and perspectives. They are being bombarded by more information from more media sources than any group of teens in history. Because they've been exposed to constant advertising their entire lives, today's teens readily form brand opinions that will continue to influence their purchase decisions into their adult years.

> Besides representing a new baby boom, today's teenagers have an income that enables discretionary spending. But that's not all. According to *Teen People,* teenagers' influence on purchases made by other people—such as parents and grandparents—represents an even larger amount of spending than their own.

This book focuses on advertising. Young people usually acknowledge the pervasiveness of advertising but tend to deny that advertising affects them. Teenagers are especially attractive to advertisers because teenagers spend most of their income on heavily advertised consumer products and services, because they strongly influence purchasing decisions by older adults, and because teenagers are beginning to develop life-long habits and brand loyalties. Teenagers, therefore, are carefully studied by the advertising industry; teenagers must respond in kind.

The guiding principle of this book is that the study of advertising can be used to teach critical-thinking skills. The units in this book provide students with information about advertising as a marketing medium, as a source of information, and as a source of social and cultural exchange. The activities require students to describe this new information and apply it in varied exercises. Students will analyze and evaluate advertising techniques and the effect advertising has on how we identify ourselves. Ultimately, this book strives to make students more informed and more discerning consumers of advertising, and more critical thinkers.

CALVIN AND HOBBES © Watterson. Reprinted with permission of UNIVERSAL PRESS SYNDICATE. All rights reserved.

To the Student

ADVERTISERS WANT YOUR attention! The reason is simple—advertisers want your money. It is estimated that Americans between the ages of 12 and 17 spend nearly $100 billion a year. Overall, teenagers in the United States spend an average of about $104 each week.

You are also seen by advertisers as being strongly brand loyal. This means that you are willing to pay more for certain brands that are perceived as cool by you and your friends. Advertising research also indicates that teenagers develop purchasing habits that may continue for many years, perhaps for the rest of their lives. You might feel that you personally are immune to the power of advertising, and that you are wise to what advertisers are up to. If so, look around your home, and count how many heavily advertised products you find.

The purpose of this book is to

- present you with methods for evaluating the quality of the information that advertising provides

- encourage you to investigate the effect advertising has on you and those around you

- help you become more knowledgeable about how advertisers get your attention, what messages they want you to receive, and sometimes, what advertisers don't want you to know about advertising

There are probably several words in this book that you are not familiar with. You will find a glossary at the back of the book. Words that are defined in the glossary appear in bold type when first used in the book.

The objectives of this unit are to help students

- understand the relationship between mass production, mass marketing, and mass media
- recognize that advertising evolves as society changes
- assess the economic consequences of advertising
- understand the basic structure of the advertising industry today

In this Unit . . .

The Evolution of Advertising asks students to discuss changes in advertising with older adults.

Puffery helps students recognize empty promises and specious comparisons.

The U.S Government and Advertising has students assess the use of advertising by the federal government.

Reach and Frequency requires students to distinguish among different types of consumer products and the different methods of advertising used to sell them.

Brand Loyalty and Consumer Involvement helps students understand the role that advertising plays in creating consumer perceptions about goods in the marketplace.

Prescription Drugs and Advertising allows students to evaluate the consequences that the heavy advertising of products has on consumer prices.

Advertising and Pseudo-Events introduces students to one form of stealth marketing frequently used by advertisers.

OCCASIONALLY, WE SEE advertisements that promote a category of product rather than a specific brand. For example, the "Got Milk?" advertisements are paid for by many milk companies and do not advertise a particular brand of milk. These types of advertisements are rare, however. Most advertisements are for particular brands of products. Branding, as identified by a name (such as Pepsi) or a **logo** (a symbol, such as the Nike swoosh), has been around for many years. However, branding did not become common until the late 1800s. Before that time, products were often sold generically, which means without a brand. For example, in the 1850s, somebody would go to the store and simply ask for sugar, instead of asking for a particular brand of sugar.

The industrial revolution of the 1800s brought mass-manufacturing of both products and packaging. New machines allowed companies to make hundreds of items in the same time it took to make a single item only a few years before. Since manufacturers could now mass-produce products, there was a need to mass-market those products.

> **"Advertisers are constantly looking for and experimenting with new ways to get us to buy their products."**

The Four P's

The marketing business has four primary concerns, usually called the Four P's: product, price, place, and promotion.

Product is the item sold, whether a tangible good (for example, a candy bar) or an intangible service (having your clothes cleaned by a dry cleaner). Today most goods are sold in packages. The package is practical (it holds the product), and it also identifies the brand of that product. Just as mass manufacturing allows for the faster and cheaper manufacturing of products, it also allows for the faster and cheaper manufacturing of boxes, bags, cans, and bottles to put those products in.

Price means the cost of the product—if the maker of a product charges too little, the company will lose money on each product sold. Too low a price also might scare away some consumers, who may believe the product must be of very poor quality if sold at too low a price. If the maker of a product charges too much, it will drive away people who might otherwise buy the product.

In the late 1800s, as new machines made it easier to make products, they also made the products cheaper, as the speed of machines made the manufacturing process more efficient. As a result, many manufacturers were able to sell products as different as sewing machines and shoes to people who either had not been able to afford them before, or who had not bought them as frequently as they now could.

Place includes distributing the product—getting the product from the manufacturer to the consumer. Distribution improved greatly in the late 1800s, as American railroads rapidly expanded. This allowed a manufacturer of a product on the west coast of the United States to sell its products on the east coast, and vice versa. For the first time, a manufacturer could have a truly national market for its products. (Some food products, such as iceberg lettuce, were specifically developed so that they could be transported by rail across the country without spoiling.) Today, place includes such issues as making certain that a consumer can obtain a product quickly and conveniently.

Promotion focuses on advertising, the subject of this book. In order to create a mass market for their mass-produced products, manufacturers began to advertise in magazines and newspapers, creating the first mass media. Mass media (*media* is the plural of *medium*) are designed to get a lot of information transmitted to a lot of people, usually as quickly as possible. Just as mechanization had made it easier and cheaper to make products and their packaging, improvements in printing technology made it easier to print relatively inexpensive newspapers and magazines, which relied on advertisements to make a profit.

The Ad Business

Early advertisements were relatively simple and did little "selling." Many of these advertisements were called tombstones, because they were nothing more than a few words on a rectangle or a square, just like a grave marker in a cemetery. They often just told consumers that a product existed and asked consumers to buy it. For example, a newspaper advertisement from the 1890s might simply say, "Please try Jones's Biscuits." In the early 1900s, advertisers realized that they had to compete more aggressively against each other, and instead of creating their own advertising, many advertisers began to seek the help of advertising agencies.

Today, most of the advertisements you see are created by advertising agencies. These firms are composed of specialized professionals; some

agencies have hundreds of employees. Advertising agency personnel include copywriters, who write the words that are read in a print advertisement or spoken in a radio or television advertisement. Commercial artists design the "look" of advertisements, choose the type of lettering that is used, the colors used, and so on. Advertising researchers try to determine what types of messages and images are most effective in selling the different types of products advertised. Advertising buyers decide which publications and broadcast media to advertise in and negotiate prices for that advertising.

Professional advertising agencies do not merely announce that a product is for sale; they try to give us a reason why we should buy the advertised product. Some of these reasons seem obvious, such as when a laundry detergent is advertised as getting your clothes clean. Some of these reasons seem more subtle. For example, look at an advertisement for a soft drink, and try to determine what reason the advertisement gives you for buying the product.

Advertising Evolves

Through the early part of the last century, advertising usually took the form of words on paper, whether in a magazine, a newspaper, a mailing, or in a **point-of-purchase advertising** display. In the 1920s, commercial radio became available as a new advertising medium, and television followed twenty years later. It was not until the 1990s that the next important advertising medium arose—the Internet. These different types of media are discussed in different sections of this book. It is important to note that each of these media—magazines, newspapers, radio, television, and the Internet—rely heavily on advertisers to make money. The price consumers pay for these media only partially pays for the cost of providing these media

The media charge advertisers for advertising based on space or time. This means that print and Internet advertising prices are based on how large the advertisement is; television and radio advertising prices are based on how long the advertisement is. The price of advertising is also based on how many people will see the advertisement. For example, a one-page advertisement in a newspaper that a thousand people read will usually be much less expensive than the same size advertisement in a newspaper read by millions of people. A thirty-second advertisement that plays on a television channel at 3 A.M. (when most of us are sleeping) will be much less expensive than a thirty-second advertisement shown during a popular program at 8 P.M. To measure the number of readers of print media (called *readership*), number of listeners of radio (*listenership*), or number of viewers of television (*viewership*), independent organizations have been established to provide reliable information to advertisers.

With the increase in advertisers and advertising media over time, it has become harder and harder for individual advertisers to break through the clutter to get—and keep—our attention. As a result, advertisers are constantly looking for and experimenting with new ways to get us to buy their products. One thing has not changed—advertisers still try to make us think we need or want whatever it is they are trying to sell.

Somewhere West of Laramie

SOMEWHERE west of Laramie there's a broncho-busting, steer-roping girl who knows what I'm talking about.

She can tell what a sassy pony, that's a cross between greased lightning and the place where it hits, can do with eleven hundred pounds of steel and action when he's going high, wide and handsome.

The truth is—the Playboy was built for her.

Built for the lass whose face is brown with the sun when the day is done of revel and romp and race.

She loves the cross of the wild and the tame.

There's a savor of links about that car—of laughter and lilt and light—a hint of old loves—and saddle and quirt. It's a brawny thing—yet a graceful thing for the sweep o' the Avenue.

Step into the Playboy when the hour grows dull with things gone dead and stale.

Then start for the land of real living with the spirit of the lass who rides, lean and rangy, into the red horizon of a Wyoming twilight.

JORDAN

JORDAN MOTOR CAR COMPANY, Inc., Cleveland, Ohio

The Evolution of Advertising -------------------------

ADVERTISING BECAME a standard part of the business world about 150 years ago. Since then, American society has changed. Most people lived on farms 150 years ago; now, most Americans live in cities. After World War II (1941–1945), more Americans started going to college than before. Technology has changed, bringing new advertising media, including television and the Internet. Technology also brought more things to advertise, such as computers and cell phones. Just as society continues to change, so does advertising.

Ask an adult or two in their forties (or older) how advertising has changed over the years. Record their answers in the spaces below. Use another sheet of paper, if necessary.

1. How has the pacing of television advertising changed? Do advertisements today seem to have a quicker pace or a slower pace than they used to? What do you think are some of the reasons for these changes?

2. How has the music used in television advertising changed? What do you think are some of the reasons for these changes?

3. How have magazine advertisements changed? What do you think are some of the reasons for these changes?

Review your interviews. Then compare the responses you received with those of your classmates. Discuss any significant differences and possible reasons for them.

Puffery -

MANY ADVERTISEMENTS rely on what is known as **puffery,** making a claim that sounds good but cannot really be evaluated. For example, if an automobile manufacturer tells you that its new car is "the hottest buy in America," how would you evaluate that claim? If a product is advertised as "America's favorite," what does that really mean? Notice that many advertisements use comparative adjectives (usually words ending in *-er,* such as *better, faster, stronger*) or superlative words (usually words ending in *-est,* such as *best, smartest, cleanest*). But such words only mean something when you know how to make the comparison. For example, if you are told that one package of gum is larger than another package, you can compare the weight of each package, or the number of pieces of gum. But how do you compare which car is hotter than another?

1. Look through newspapers and magazines and find advertisements for three different goods or services that use puffery to sell their products. Attach the advertisements to this page. Using the chart below, explain how each advertisement contains puffery.

Product	Example of puffery	Why is this puffery?

2. Why do you think puffery is used so often by advertisers?

The U.S. Government and Advertising - - - - - - - - - - - - - - -

THE FEDERAL GOVERNMENT of the United States raises most of the money it needs to operate by taxing the income of people who live and work in the United States, and by taxing corporations that do business in the United States. Many American taxpayers fall within a 28% tax bracket for most income. This means the taxpayer must give 28% of the taxable income she or he earns each year to the federal government. The government uses this money for hundreds of different purposes, including paying for the military, providing financial help to unemployed people, and helping states build highways and airports.

The U.S government also spends money on advertising. In 2000, for example, the U.S. government was the eighteenth-largest advertiser in the country, just behind McDonald's, and many millions of dollars ahead of Sony and Coca-Cola. That year, the U.S. government spent a total of $1,246,300,000 on advertising, including over $500 million on television and radio ads.

Record your answers below. Use another sheet of paper, if necessary.

1. According to the 2000 census, there are about 281 million Americans. How much did the government spend on total advertising per American that year?

2. Do you think that it is a good idea or a bad idea that our government spends so much of our money on advertising? Why?

One of the things that the U.S. government advertises is the military. The government advertises to encourage people to join the Army, Navy, Air Force, Marines, and Coast Guard.

3. Do you think that it is a good idea or a bad idea for our government to advertise for people to join the military? Why?

4. In this chart, list two other things that you think would be important for the government to advertise. Then explain why this is important.

Thing to advertise	Why important

Reach and Frequency -

WHEN ADVERTISERS decide how much money they want to spend to advertise a particular product, they have to decide on matters of **reach** and **frequency.** Reach is concerned with how many people see an advertisement, and in how large a geographical area. For example, the owner of a local bakery would not want to spend the money it would cost to advertise that bakery all across the country, or across the state, or maybe even throughout the entire city or town the bakery is in, because the bakery might only expect to sell its products to people in the neighborhood where it is located. On the other hand, Wrigley's advertises its chewing gum throughout the country, because many Americans chew gum, and because Wrigley's products are available everywhere in the country.

Frequency is a way of describing how many advertisements an advertiser uses, and how often. Frequency can be measured in a single medium (such as newspapers) or in a variety of media (newspapers, radio, television, magazines, billboards, and so on). Products that tend to have little brand loyalty and are purchased (and repurchased) will usually have frequent advertisements. For example, advertising for shampoos and fast food restaurants often stresses frequency.

Record your answers below. Use another sheet of paper, if necessary.

1. In this chart, list three types of products that you think should emphasize reach of advertising, trying to reach as much of the American population as possible. Then explain why advertising for each type of product would emphasize reach.

Type of product	Why reach?

2. In this chart, list three types of products that you think should emphasize frequency of advertising, trying to run as many advertisements as often as possible. Then explain why advertising for each type of product would emphasize frequency.

Type of product	Why frequency?

Brand Loyalty and Consumer Involvement - - - - - - - - - - - - -

BRAND LOYALTY, or the lack of brand loyalty, is an important concern for advertisers. Brand loyalty means that a lot of people who use a product have a favorite brand and may go to a little extra trouble to find it. They may even be willing to pay more for it than other brands. Some advertisers have developed brand loyalty for their products by spending millions and millions of dollars on advertising, which keeps the product's name in consumers' minds. Other companies have developed brand loyalty mostly through word of mouth; people have tried the product, like it, and recommend it to their friends. Many products have developed brand loyalty through a combination of these processes.

List three brands of products that you or people you know are very loyal to.

1.

2.

3.

List three reasons why people might be loyal to a particular brand.

1.

2.

3.

List three types of products that you or people you know have very little brand loyalty to.

1.

2.

3.

List three reasons why people might not care which brand of product they buy.

1.

2.

3.

(continued)

Brand Loyalty and Consumer Involvement - - - - - - - - - - - -

Consumer involvement is a marketing concept that examines how much time people think about a product before they purchase it. For example, since a car is an expensive investment, the decision to buy a car has high consumer involvement. Many car buyers do research in magazines and on the Internet before buying a car and may investigate several cars before making a decision. Low consumer involvement is associated with impulse or routine purchases. For example, a person might buy the cheapest brand of paper towel, or the brand that has the biggest store display. Low involvement purchases are often influenced by point-of-purchase advertising.

Whether a product is a high involvement or low involvement item should not be confused with brand loyalty. For example, some people will buy a particular brand of paper towels because that is the brand they always buy (without really thinking about why), and some people buy whatever brand is cheapest, or whichever brand they see first.

Record your answers below. Use another sheet of paper, if necessary.

1. In this chart, list three types of products that you would consider to be high involvement items. Then explain why each is a high involvement item.

Item	Why high involvement?

2. What sorts of messages do you think advertisers for high involvement items should give in their advertisements?

3. In this chart, list three types of products that you would consider to be low involvement items. Then explain why each is a low involvement item.

Item	Why low involvement?

4. What sorts of messages do you think advertisers for low involvement items should give in their advertisements?

Prescription Drugs and Advertising - - - - - - - - - - - - - - - - - -

THERE ARE TWO basic forms of medical drugs. Prescription drugs require a note from a doctor in order to be purchased from a pharmacy. Over-the-counter drugs can be purchased without a prescription at a pharmacy, grocery store, and so on. Drugs that require a prescription are considered to be particularly dangerous if misused. To prevent misuse, the federal government requires that a person has the advice of a doctor before buying prescription drugs.

For many years, companies that make prescription drugs were not allowed to advertise those drugs on television without giving many warnings about problems that might occur when taking those drugs. The warnings were usually so long that it cost too much money for prescription drug makers to advertise on television. Those drug companies relied instead on magazine and news-paper advertisements.

Drug companies also relied heavily on salespeople who would call on doctors who prescribed drugs. (Notice when you go to a doctor's office how much advertising she or he has in the office for different drugs, on things such as coffee cups and notepads.) This type of advertising is called **push marketing,** aimed at the people responsible for the product being distributed (the doctor) rather than the end user of the product (the patient).

In 1997, the U.S. Food and Drug Administration (FDA) changed its rule and said that prescription drugs could be advertised on television, as long as the advertisements told of ways that people could get more information about those drugs. Other sources of information include an Internet web site or a toll-free telephone number. This type of advertising, called "direct-to-consumer" advertising, is a type of **pull marketing.** It is aimed at the end user of the product (the patient) rather than the person who helps distribute the product (the doctor).

1. List a product that uses push marketing. (Look at some ads on television or in magazines and newspapers for clues.) Why does this product use push marketing?

2. List a product that uses pull marketing. (Hint: Think about things sold in the grocery store.) Why does this product use pull marketing?

(continued)

Prescription Drugs and Advertising - - - - - - - - - - - - - - - - -

Since the FDA's rule changed in 1997, we have seen many advertisements for prescription drugs on television, and the amount of money people spend on prescription drugs has increased significantly.

3. Many of the most popular prescription drugs today are also the most heavily advertised. Explain why you think this is so. When you buy a product that is heavily advertised, who really is paying for the advertising of that product? Explain.

Some people think it was a good idea when the FDA changed its regulations and allowed prescription drug makers to advertise more easily on television. Some people think it was a bad idea.

4. Describe one reason why direct-to-consumer drug advertising is a bad idea. Describe one reason why direct-to-consumer drug advertising is a good idea. Overall, do you think direct-to-consumer drug advertising is a good idea or bad idea? Explain why you answered the way you did.

Advertising and Pseudo-Events -

THE PREFIX *pseudo-* means "fake" (for example, the author Samuel Clemens published books under the pseudonym, or fake name, Mark Twain). Advertisers often try to create **pseudo-events,** or fake news events, that focus on their product. For example, the Super Bowl game each year, which sports fans consider to be a real event, also includes the first showing of expensively made advertisements that often feature major celebrities and special effects. These advertisements usually receive lots of attention from the news media before and after they are shown for the first time.

Another example of a pseudo-event that you may recall from several years ago involved candy. The makers of M&Ms candy asked consumers to vote on what color to change the light brown shade of candy to—the choices were purple and blue. Blue was the winner, and the makers of M&Ms paid to have the New York City's Empire State Building lit up in blue at night to celebrate the winner. This pseudo-event received major coverage in the news media, including television and newspapers. Generating hype around pseudo-events is one form of **stealth marketing.** Stealth marketing occurs when an advertiser engages in marketing activities but tries to make it look like it is not.

1. Find another example of a pseudo-event, by paying careful attention to television programs or newspaper and magazine articles for a week or so. What other example did you find?

2. Explain why this is a pseudo-event.

3. Review the Ad Buzz material for this unit. Why do you think the media often willingly cooperate with advertisers who try to create these fake events?

The objectives of this unit are to help students

- recognize the pervasiveness of advertising in American society
- understand why advertisers are strongly attracted to consumers in certain age groups and less attracted to consumers in other age groups
- examine empty claims made in advertising
- explore the use of celebrity endorsements in advertising

In this Unit . . .

Tobacco Advertising and Teens has students confront past efforts of major tobacco companies to market cigarettes to teenagers.

Advertising at School helps students understand the pervasiveness of advertising in American society.

"Let the Product be the Hero": Advertising and Problems introduces students to a standard advertising technique—highlighting a problem and offering the product as the solution.

What Is the Ad Really Saying? provides students with a chance to learn how different products are targeted to different consumers.

Advertising and Age asks students to discuss advertising issues with senior citizens.

Celebrities and Ads allows students to explore the role that athletes and entertainers play in advertising.

Advertising and the Hierarchy of Needs has students apply the different stages of Maslow's Hierarchy of Needs to the advertising of consumer goods.

Ad Buzz

THE AVERAGE AMERICAN sees about 3,000 advertisements a day. By high school graduation, you will have watched about 350,000 television commercials. This may sound like it is too high a figure, but consider the fact that American businesses spend over $130 billion on advertising each year. Worldwide, $620 billion is spent on marketing annually—about $120 for every man, woman, and child on the planet. Whether it is effective or not, a lot of money is being spent on advertising.

What is an advertisement? Sometimes, advertisements are obvious—a thirty-second commercial on television, a full-page advertisement in a magazine, or a billboard on the side of a highway. Sometimes, advertisements are more subtle. This can include types of stealth marketing—sneaky marketing that does not look like advertising, but is. Just a few examples:

> **"The average American sees about 3,000 advertisements a day."**

- Advertisers pay movie and television producers to show their product being used by the characters in a movie or television show; this practice is called **product placement.**

- Videos on MTV and other music-oriented channels are basically advertisements for recording companies.

- Fashion magazines such as *Seventeen* contain articles about celebrities that tell the reader what brands of cosmetics those celebrities wear; the cosmetic companies pay to have that information published.

- *The Price Is Right* and other television game shows feature dozens of name-brand products on every program.

- Corporations sponsor events, such as football games (The FedEx Orange Bowl). Even Pope John Paul II's visit to Mexico in 1999 was sponsored by Frito-Lay and Pepsi!

Advertisers and Teens

Advertisers divide consumers into categories called **demographics** and **psychographics.** Demographics are statistics that group people by age, gender, ethnicity, geography, and income. Psychographics are statistics that group people by their interests, attitudes, values, and habits (including buying habits). Teenagers are among the favorite demographic groups for advertisers. This is not because they like you! Rather, it is because they want to prey on the vulnerability of teenagers, many of whom are unsure about themselves. Advertisers also want to help teenagers establish lifelong buying habits, because teenagers have many years of consumption ahead of them.

Gathering Information

In this age of computers, companies go to a lot of trouble to gather demographic and psychographic information on consumers. For example, when someone buys a walkman or a cell phone, it comes with a product registration card that asks questions about why the person bought the product, when and how the buyer will use the product, what advertisements the buyer may have seen about the product, what interests/hobbies the buyer has, even how much money the buyer makes. Many consumers ignore these cards, but others fill out all the information and mail them in.

Another technique used to gather information about consumers is the use of contests. Products aimed at teenagers often have contests that require people to reveal information similar to that asked on the product registration card. Most people who enter the contest will not win, but the advertiser now has more information about people interested in its products. Sometimes, advertisers will run different types of advertisements at the same time, to see which type of advertisement gets the most response. This is a question of **quantitative research,** because it examines the number of people who respond to an advertisement. In a process referred to as **data mining,** advertisers examine the information they collect and see if different types of people respond to different types of advertisements. This is called **qualitative research,** because it examines types of people rather than simply the number of people who respond to an advertisement.

The activities in this section are designed to help you learn more about how advertisers design advertisements based on the needs and wants of different groups of consumers.

Tobacco Advertising and Teens ----------------------

IN 1998, THE largest tobacco companies in the United States settled a series of lawsuits with the governments of 46 states and five U.S. territories. The tobacco companies agreed to pay approximately $206 billion over 25 years for tobacco prevention. In an effort to reduce children and teenagers being exposed to tobacco advertising, the settlement also required tobacco companies to remove all billboard advertising and advertising in sports arenas by 1999. By 2000, the tobacco companies promised to stop using cartoon characters to sell cigarettes and stop distributing "gear" such as shirts and hats with tobacco logos.

The settlement also saw tobacco companies agree to make many of their internal documents available to the public. One of these documents came from R.J. Reynolds, the maker of Camel, Winston, Salem, and many other brands of cigarettes. (R.J. Reynolds sold over 90 billion cigarettes in 2001.) This document, written in 1973, was seen as one of the "smoking guns" by those who accused tobacco companies of intentionally directing advertising at teenagers, a claim that tobacco companies had repeatedly denied. In its discussion of "Psychological Effects" the R.J. Reynolds document says:

> The smoking-health controversy does not appear important to [teenagers] because, psychologically, at eighteen, one is immortal. Further, if the desire to be daring is part of the motivation to start smoking, the alleged risk of smoking may actually make smoking attractive. Finally, if the "older" establishment is preaching against smoking, the anti-establishment sentiment . . . would cause the young to want to be defiant and smoke. Thus a new brand aimed at the young group should not in any way be promoted as a "health" brand, and perhaps should carry some implied risk. In this sense, the warning label on the package may be a plus.

Suppose a tobacco company wanted to introduce a new cigarette called "The Dude's Death-sticks." The label on the package shows a skeleton with blood-shot eyes smoking a cigarette. In addition to the surgeon general's warning about the health risks of smoking (which are required by federal law), the package has a large warning that "These things will kill you dead, my friend." Advertisements in magazines feature a picture of a grandmotherly-looking woman who looks upset, and who is quoted as saying "No kids of mine are going to smoke these things, and if they do, I'll give them a good whuppin'."

1. Would you be interested in trying these cigarettes? Why or why not?

2. Do you think some of your friends would be interested in trying these cigarettes? Why or why not?

(continued)

Tobacco Advertising and Teens -

In 1971, cigarette advertisements on television were banned by federal law. Certainly, this policy has cost broadcasters many millions of dollars over the years, since cigarette companies spend a lot of money on advertising.

3. If the federal government changed its mind and decided to allow cigarette advertisements to be shown on television, do you think some people who do not smoke might begin to? Explain.

4. If you do not smoke, do you think that seeing frequent tobacco advertisements on television would make you more likely to smoke, or not? Explain.

5. If the federal government allowed cigarette advertisements on television, do you think that people who already smoke would smoke more? Explain.

6. If you already smoke now, do you think that seeing frequent tobacco advertisements on television would make you more likely to smoke more, or not? Explain.

Advertising at School -

LOOK AROUND your classroom. Count how many advertisements you can find. Examples include brand names on school supplies, computer and audio/visual equipment, and, of course, clothing.

1. How many advertisements did you find?

2. How many advertisements did you find on clothing that are for the brand of that clothing?

3. How many advertisements did you find on clothing that are for things other than the brand of clothing? (This includes the names of colleges and sports teams.)

4. Are those people who are wearing advertising getting paid by the advertisers to advertise their product? Or vice versa?

5. Why do people wear advertising?

6. Who is more likely to wear clothing with advertising—people your age, or people your parents' age?

7. Why do you think this is the case?

"Let the Product be the Hero": Advertising and Problems -

ONE OF THE MOST common slogans among people in the advertising business is "let the product be the hero." One of the ways advertisers get us to buy things is to point out a problem we may have (whether real or imagined) and offer their product as a solution to that problem.

For example, an advertisement for a cleaning product may show pictures of a bathroom or kitchen before and after using the product. An advertisement for disposable diapers might emphasize that the product does not leak. Let's call these "physical" problems, because they are situations that involve some sort of physical change.

Other advertisements focus on personal or "social" problems. These include situations in which the advertised product is shown as helping the user avoid embarrassment, sadness, or loneliness. For example, the typical mouthwash advertisement talks about social problems associated with bad breath.

Find three advertisements that identify a problem. Examine how the advertised product is offered as a solution. Fill in the chart with information about these ads.

Name of product	Problem— physical or social?	Solution	Is the situation realistic? Explain.

What Is the Ad Really Saying? -

TO HELP MAKE a product and its advertising memorable, many advertisements rely on a slogan, also called a **tagline.** This is often presented at the end of a television or radio advertisement, or at the bottom of a newspaper or magazine advertisement. Examples include McDonald's "We Love to See You Smile" and Ford Truck's "Built Ford Tough."

Fill in the chart below. Use another sheet of paper, if necessary. List three products and their slogans. For each slogan, write what you think the slogan means and then decide whether or not the slogan makes sense to you, and why.

Product name	Slogan	Does slogan make sense? Explain.

Now find two advertisements for a product that you do not have any need for.

- a product for males if you are a female (or for females if you are male)
- a product that is for somebody much older than you

For each of these products, fill in the appropriate chart below. After you have written *your* responses, ask somebody who the product is meant for to explain how *he or she* interprets the slogan.

Product used by a member of the opposite gender

Name of product:	
Slogan:	
Does the slogan make sense to you? Explain.	
Does the slogan make sense to the intended consumer? Explain.	

Product used by an older person

Name of product:	
Slogan:	
Does the slogan make sense to you? Explain.	
Does the slogan make sense to the intended consumer? Explain.	

Advertising and Age -------------------------------

THE AVERAGE SENIOR citizen (a person age sixty and older) watches more hours of television each week than the average teen. However, you will notice that very few advertisements on television are directed at senior citizens, while many advertisements are aimed at teenagers. Television shows and television networks that are aimed at teenagers are more attractive to advertisers than programs that are watched mostly by older adults. For example, even though the *Red Skelton Show* was the seventh most watched show in the United States (and had been consistently in the top ten over the previous years), CBS cancelled it in 1970, because Skelton drew an older audience. More recently, *Dr. Quinn, Medicine Woman* experienced a similar fate.

1. Why do you think advertisers are often less interested in older audiences?

2. Ask a senior citizen why he or she thinks advertisers are less interested in older audiences. Record the answer here.

3. Ask that senior citizen how she or he feels about being less attractive to advertisers. Record the answer here.

4. Why do you think advertisers are more interested in teens?

5. Do you view advertisers' interest in you as a good thing or a bad thing? Explain.

Celebrities and Ads

MANY PROFESSIONAL ATHLETES, who are paid millions of dollars to play their sport, actually make much more money for appearing in ads for various products. These appearances in ads are referred to as endorsements. An endorsement means that the athlete is seen by consumers as saying the product is a good one. Sometimes the advertised product is related to the sport—for example, Tiger Woods appearing in ads for golf equipment, or Michael Jordan appearing in ads for Gatorade. Sometimes, however, there is no relationship between sports and the product being advertised. Woods appears in ads for Buick, and Jordan appears in ads for Hanes underwear. Obviously, the advertisers who pay athletes to endorse their products believe that these endorsements will sell more of their products.

Record your answers below. Use another sheet of paper, if necessary.

1. Why do you think an advertisement featuring a professional athlete, for a product unrelated to sports, helps sell that product?

2. Besides athletes, what other types of celebrities appear in ads?

3. In this chart, list two of your favorite athletes, musicians, and actors right now. Then list any products each endorses.

	Celebrities	Products
Athletes		
Musicians		
Actors		

4. Does the fact that these people associate themselves with certain products make you more or less likely to buy the products? Explain.

5. Who ends up paying the money that celebrities get for appearing in these ads? Explain.

Advertising and the Hierarchy of Needs ---------------

ABRAHAM MASLOW was an American psychologist who studied people's needs. He identified certain categories of needs and ranked them. His rankings are referred to as Maslow's Hierarchy of Needs. (A hierarchy is a method of ranking things by degree of importance.)

- Physiological needs come first. These are basic needs, such as food and water.
- Safety comes next; this includes a sense of security. Safety can include a feeling of financial security—the need to know that the bills are going to be paid.
- Psychological needs follow. These are social needs that include love, acceptance by others, and the feeling of belonging.
- Esteem is the next level. This means feeling respected by others, and self-respect.
- At the top of Maslow's hierarchy is something he called self-actualization. This is the need to fulfill oneself, to become all that one is capable of being.

Maslow's Hierarchy of Needs is often shown as a pyramid, with the larger, lower levels representing the more basic needs and the upper part representing the need for self-actualization.

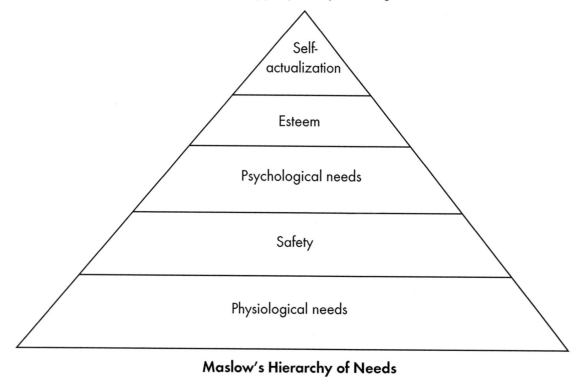

Maslow's Hierarchy of Needs

(continued)

Advertising and the Hierarchy of Needs -------------

Maslow said that if the needs that were lower in his hierarchy were not met, then it would very difficult or impossible to fulfill needs higher up the rankings. (For example, if you were starving, would you have the time to worry about whether or not people thought you were cool?) It also becomes harder to meet the needs as one moves up the pyramid—food and water are easier to get than self-actualization.

Find five advertisements, each of which appeals to one of the needs in Maslow's Hierarchy of Needs. If it is a magazine or newspaper advertisement, attach it to this page. If it is a television or radio advertisement, describe the advertisement. Use another sheet of paper, if necessary.

Physiological needs

Name of product:

How does the ad appeal to this need?

Safety

Name of product:

How does the ad appeal to this need?

Psychological needs

Name of product:

How does the ad appeal to this need?

Esteem

Name of product:

How does the ad appeal to this need?

Self-actualization

Name of product:

How does the ad appeal to this need?

The objectives of this unit are to help students

- understand how advertisers attempt to prey on consumers' self-esteem issues
- evaluate the pernicious effects of fashion advertising on women's body image
- recognize the pervasiveness of advertising in American culture
- assess the impact advertising has on women's health issues
- develop creative advertising approaches to social problems

In this Unit . . .

What's the Message? requires students to scrutinize and deconstruct the language of advertising.

Consumption as Self-Expression? has students examine how advertisers appeal to teenagers' desire for autonomy.

Why Do Advertisers Want Us to Be Sad? allows students to evaluate the effect advertising has on women's body image.

So Many Shampoos! lets students assess how much advertising they have been exposed to.

The Internet: The Next Frontier introduces students to the techniques by which Internet advertisers try to gather data about teenagers.

Cigarettes and Gender has students examine the imagery of cigarette advertising and call on their own creativity to generate a response.

ALTHOUGH A FEMALE is born a female, she is not born knowing how females are supposed to act, or not act, in society. Young females are taught "feminine behavior" by their family, by society, and, to some degree, by advertising. (Guys, you go through the same process that females do!)

The role of women in society has dramatically changed over the years. This is not always apparent in advertising, however. Much (but not all) of the advertising directed toward females tells them that they need to worry about their looks, worry about their weight, and obey males. Even though many females know that these messages are wrong, these messages are so frequent and widespread that it is almost impossible to ignore them.

> **"Advertisers offer their product as a solution to our problems."**

Advertisers want people to buy things. If we are happy with the way things are, then we are less likely to buy things. Advertisers know this, so they subtly try to make us unhappy—unhappy with our appearance, our relationships, our situation in life in general—so that we will be more interested in buying advertised products. Advertisers offer their product as a solution to our problems. If we do not know that we have a problem, then advertisers are more than happy to create one for us.

What's the Message? -

Look at three advertisements for women's cosmetics or "beauty aids" in magazines such as *Seventeen, Glamour,* or *Cosmopolitan.* What do these advertisements tell the audience is important in a female? Use the chart below to answer this question.

Type of product	What ad says is important	Is this important? Explain.

Consumption as Self-Expression? - - - - - - - - - - - - - - - - - -

Advertisements for Tommy Hilfiger's Tommy Girl perfume claim that the product is "a declaration of independence." Stetson's American Original perfume's advertisements tell readers that "you have the right to be you," that you should "express your true self." The headline of an advertisement for Sanrio's Hello Kitty items says "Free to be me."

Look through women's fashion magazines and find three ads aimed at female teens that claim the product helps the consumer to be herself, to be one of a kind, to be special, or to express herself.

Record your answers below. Use another sheet of paper, if necessary.

1. In this chart, list each product and its advertising claim.

Product	Advertising claim

2. Why is this type of message so common in advertising directed at teens?

3. Why is this type of message actually dishonest?

4. Do some people buy certain things because they think those things give a message to other people about them? Explain, using examples from your experience.

You or one of your friends has probably bought something, such as a type of clothing or a CD by a certain musician, because other friends had that item. This is probably an example of peer pressure, and it occurs among both males and females.

5. Look through some fashion magazines aimed at female teens and find three examples of ads that use peer pressure to sell the product. Note that sometimes the message is in the ad's words, and sometimes the message is in the picture.
   In this chart, list the product and describe how the ad uses peer pressure.

Product	How peer pressure is used

Why Do Advertisers Want Us to Be Sad? - - - - - - - - - - -

THE AVERAGE American woman is 5 feet 4 inches tall and weighs 142 pounds. The average fashion model is 5 feet 9 inches tall and weighs 110 pounds. More than 75% of American women say that they "feel fat."

Record your answers below. Use another sheet of paper, if necessary.

1. How much less does the average fashion model weigh than the average woman? How much less is that as a percentage?

2. How do you think those models stay so thin?

3. Do pictures of thin models make the average female reader feel good or bad about herself? Explain.

4. If you are female, how do pictures of thin models make you feel? If you are male, ask a female friend or relative how pictures of thin models make her feel.

5. Why do you think advertisers usually choose thin models?

6. In this chart, list three different types of advertisers who benefit from showing thin models. Then explain how the advertisers benefit.

Types of advertisers	How they benefit

You may know that anorexia nervosa is a psychological illness that causes lack of appetite in people, primarily young women. Those who suffer from anorexia refuse to maintain body weight that is at or above the minimally normal weight for age and height. Bulimia nervosa is the practice of binge eating, often followed by forcing oneself to vomit.

Nobody is born anorexic or bulimic; the messages people receive from society and advertising often contribute to the development of these disorders.

7. How does the constant use of abnormally thin fashion models by advertisers contribute to anorexia and bulimia?

So Many Shampoos! -

Record your answers below. Use another sheet of paper, if necessary.

1. List below all the brand names of hair shampoos that you can think of. After you have written your list, take your list to a grocery store or drugstore and count how many brands of shampoo there are in the store.

2. How many brands were you able to list?

3. How many brands did you find in the store?

4. Why do you think there are so many different brands of shampoo?

5. Look on some of the labels of different brands of shampoo—does a different company make every brand, or do some companies make many different brands?

Companies that make shampoo spend over $300 million on advertising each year.

6. What role do you think advertising played in helping you to identify brands?

7. To whom is most shampoo advertising directed?

8. Why do you think this audience is targeted?

The Internet: The Next Frontier -

THERE IS A VARIETY of Internet sites directed at female teens. These include gURL.com, ecrush.com, and mtvgirl.com. Even though these sites are directed toward teenage females, each of these sites is actually put together by people who are twenty- and thirty-something years old. These sites rely on **cool hunting** to find out what teenage females are interested in, how they talk, and how advertisers can get their attention.

1. Visit these web sites, or other similar web sites you know of. In the chart below, list the web site and describe three ways each tries to be cool.

Web site	Examples of cool		
	1.	2.	3.

Each of these is a commercial site that allows the visitor to become a member. By asking visitors to join, the web site's owner gathers information about those visitors.

2. Explain how offering the web site as some sort of club might make that web site attractive to visitors.

Cigarettes and Gender -

YOUNG WOMEN are more likely to smoke than young men are. One reason is that most females want to stay thin. Cigarettes have long been considered a no-calorie substitute for eating. The leading cigarette brand aimed at women, Virginia Slims, even highlights this in its name. One study at Harvard Medical School found that females who are unhappy about their appearance are twice as likely to think about using tobacco as females who are comfortable with their looks.

The fact that cigarette ads frequently appear in fashion magazines that feature very thin fashion models helps the cigarette industry. (Are you surprised that Kate Moss is a chain-smoker?)

1. Find three different ads in fashion magazines that show cigarette smoking to be fashionable or even sexy. (Remember, sometimes the message is in the words of the ad, and sometimes it is in the pictures!) In the chart below, list each brand of cigarette. Then describe how the ad makes smoking appear to be fashionable or sexy:

Cigarette brand	How shown to be fashionable/sexy

2. Now find three ads for "masculine" brands of cigarettes. In the chart below, list the name of the brand, where you found the ad, and what the ad suggests about smoking.

Cigarette brand	Source of ad	What ad suggests

(continued)

Cigarettes and Gender -

You have probably heard all sorts of information in school, at home, and in the media about how cigarettes are bad for you. In Unit 2, we looked at how discussing health issues related to smoking may actually only encourage teens to smoke. Part of the problem may be, as with other examples we have seen, people who are much older than teenagers are trying to learn how to be cool as they try to communicate with teenagers.

Whether or not you smoke cigarettes, think about the best way to advertise to get teenagers to quit.

3. Where would you advertise? Why?

4. What images would your advertisements show? Why?

5. What words, if any, would be shown in print and television ads and spoken in television and radio ads? Why?

The objectives of this unit are to help students

- understand how advertisers exploit ritualized traditional notions of manhood
- design and administer a survey, and tabulate the results
- examine how the literary device of personification is used in the advertising of products
- explore the concept of prestige pricing and the perceived need of many consumers to pay a premium for a product
- investigate the role of sports as a marketing device

In this Unit . . .

Beer and Manhood lets students explore the use of masculine rituals as a theme of beer advertising.

Athletic Shoes Usually Aren't Cheap! introduces students to the concept of prestige pricing and asks them to examine their own willingness to succumb to it.

Cigarettes, Booze, and Sports has students investigate the reasons cigarette and beer makers associate themselves with sports.

Are You Tough Enough to Drive a Truck? lets students evaluate the literary device of masculine personification in truck advertising.

Dealing with the Munchies is a suggested group project that allows students to create, administer, and tabulate a survey for a hypothetical new snack food.

Shaving and Experiential Marketing introduces students to the most recent trend in consumer product advertising.

BOYS LEARN TO BECOME men as they grow. Many of the messages about masculinity come from older men that young males are close to—fathers, family members, teachers, and friends—men who often serve as role models for boys. But how much time do young males spend in the company of these role models, and how much time do young males spend in the presence of advertising? Children between the ages of 2 and 11 watch an average of 10 hours of television a week (and remember, most of them have to go to bed early). Television viewing varies from boy to boy, but the reality is that many American males learn what it means to be a man in part

> "Many American males learn what it means to be a man in part from advertising."

from advertising. As males get older, they begin reading magazines, often about sports, cars, and music, and may sometimes sneak a peak at "girlie" magazines. All of these magazines contain dozens of advertisements, usually aimed at men.

These advertisements are for such products as razors and shaving creams, alcohol, cars and trucks, and tobacco. Advertisements often offer the product as a way to define oneself. If you look around, you will notice that a lot of adults choose to buy cars or trucks that they believe tells other people something about themselves. For example, automakers found that many parents with children did not want to be seen as "old" and that they wanted to drive a vehicle that could hold the entire family but still look "cool." This is

part of the reason that sports utility vehicles (SUVs) have become so popular over the past few years. Notice that beer, a product often associated with men, rarely emphasizes how the product tastes in advertisements; there is usually something else going on.

MISTER OTIS

REGRETS

HE DIDN'T USE KREML!

DON'T LET THIS HAPPEN TO YOU

Is your comb full of hair every time you use it?

Are your shoulders covered with dandruff?

Does your hair refuse to behave unless it is "plastered down"?

Then you should try Kreml. This wonderful new tonic checks falling hair and removes dandruff.

It makes the hair behave without that gigolo look.

It leaves no barber shop odor in its wake.

After a dip in the sea or a day in the open it removes every trace of sea-salt, stickiness and grime.

The whole country is turning to Kreml.

Try it. You will swear by this tonic too.

TRY KREML SHAMPOO, TOO!
Made with 80% pure olive oil. It simply billows with cleansing, purifying lather.

KREML
FOR FALLING HAIR AND DANDRUFF

Beer and Manhood -------------------------------

SOME PEOPLE HAVE SAID that beer advertisements tell the intended audience that drinking beer is a sign of manhood. We often see beer advertising associated with guy stuff—going to a football game, working at a construction site, shooting pool with the gang. Beer advertisements often are set inside bars and clubs, with the implied message being that beer helps people have a good time. For men, fun is supposed to mean being accepted by the guys while also being attractive to the ladies.

Find a beer advertisement in a magazine that portrays beer drinking as a sign of manhood, cut out the advertisement, and attach it to this page.

1. Explain how the advertisement you selected tries to appeal to a viewer's sense of manhood.

2. Explain why you think beer companies believe that this is a good way to sell their product.

Find a print advertisement for a brand of beer or watch some beer advertisements on television that use sex (including flirting) to sell that beer.

3. What connection is the intended audience supposed to make between the product and the sexual message?

4. Is that connection necessarily an intelligent one to make? Explain.

Athletic Shoes Usually Aren't Cheap! - - - - - - - - - - - - - - -

Record your answers below. Use another sheet of paper, if necessary.

1. List all the brands of sneakers/athletic shoes that you can think of. Then go to a sporting goods store and count how many brands of shoes there are in the store.

2. How many brands were you able to list?

3. How many brands did you find in the store?

4. What role do you think advertising played in helping you to identify brands?

5. To whom do you think most sneaker/athletic shoe advertising is directed toward?

6. Why do you think this audience is targeted?

Price is one of the main concerns of marketing. "Prestige pricing" means the high price of an item brings a positive image to the product and to the person who buys it. For example, some people drive Corvettes because they want to show they can afford to spend $50,000 on a car.

7. Prestige pricing is a major marketing element of many brands of athletic shoes. Why?

8. If you were going to buy a pair of shoes at a store like Foot Locker, would you try to find the least expensive pair? Why or why not?

9. Would you be willing to buy a brand of athletic shoes you never heard of if they were a few dollars less than the heavily advertised brands? Why or why not?

10. Would you be willing to buy a brand of athletic shoes you never heard of if they were half the price of the heavily advertised brands? Why or why not?

11. If you pay more for a heavily advertised brand of shoe than an unadvertised brand, who is really paying for the cost of advertising that shoe? Explain.

It is likely that at least once you have had a disagreement with an older family adult who thought you were spending too much money on shoes or some other clothing item.

12. How have you defended your decision in this situation?

Cigarettes, Booze, and Sports - - - - - - - - - - - - - - - - - - -

ALTHOUGH CIGARETTES AND BEER are not logically associated with sports, we have long seen these products advertised in sports settings. The 1998 settlement between major tobacco companies and 46 states is discussed in Unit 2. One of the requirements of the settlement was the removal of cigarette advertising from sports arenas and stadiums. Although cigarette ads on television have been illegal for years, anybody watching a televised athletic event probably saw numerous cigarette ads inside the arena or stadium, and most facilities today have ads for beer. For many years, Virginia Slims cigarettes were the main sponsor of the professional Women's Tennis Association. We still have the Winston Cup Series in NASCAR auto racing today.

Another NASCAR racing series carries Busch Beer's name. Rusty Wallace drives a NASCAR racing car that advertises Miller Lite Beer. Major league baseball's St. Louis Cardinals play at Busch Stadium, the Milwaukee Brewers play at Miller Field, and the Colorado Rockies play at Coors Field. Hockey's Montreal Canadiens play in Le Centre Molson.

Record your answers below. Use another sheet of paper, if necessary.

1. Why do you think some people are upset that beer, which contains alcohol, is associated with automobile racing?

2. Do you agree or disagree with those people? Explain.

3. Why are some people upset that beer is associated with other sports?

4. Do you agree or disagree with those people? Explain.

5. Why are some people upset that cigarettes are associated with some sports?

6. Do you agree or disagree with those people? Explain.

7. Do you think that sponsorship of sporting events by beer and cigarette companies is a form of stealth marketing or not? Explain.

Are You Tough Enough to Drive a Truck? - - - - - - - - - - - - -

LET US REVIEW two words that you probably have heard before. *Machismo* refers to a strong, sometimes exaggerated masculinity. Machismo is displayed through physical strength, aggressiveness, and manliness. (*Macho* is a related word.)

Personification describes nonhuman objects in human terms. We often refer to the United States flag as "she." If a machine breaks down, people may say, "it just doesn't want to go anymore," as if a machine can make choices. Both of these are examples of personification.

Advertising for most trucks is directed toward male consumers. Chevrolet trucks are "like a rock" and "hardworking" and "rugged." Ford trucks are "built Ford tough" and are also "Dependable. Hard Working. Powerful. Capable." Ford's web site tells consumers that knowledge about its trucks is a sign of the consumer's manliness. Dodge trucks are "tough" and "powerful." Dodge tells consumers that its Ram is "one of the biggest, strongest and hardest-working trucks anywhere." Toyota asks consumers if they consider themselves "tough enough for Tacoma?" Nissan describes its trucks as "tough" and their styling "aggressive."

1. Explain why you think truck advertising uses personification.

2. Explain why you think truck advertising emphasizes macho-type qualities.

Over the last few years, car companies have been selling more and more trucks to women. Some companies, such as Ford, have asked women to tell them what features they want in trucks. Imagine you are an advertising executive for Ford, and that Ford wants to sell trucks to both men and women, without offending either gender.

3. Would you change the way Ford advertises its trucks, or leave the advertising the way it is? Explain.

Dealing with the Munchies -

MARKETING RESEARCH has shown that teenage males spend the biggest percentage of their money on food and entertainment, while teenage girls spend the biggest percentage of their money on cosmetics and clothing.

1. Find three advertisements for food products that you believe are aimed at teenage males. List the product, and next to each, explain why you think the advertisement is aimed specifically at teenage males.

Product	Why teenage males?

Frito-Lay, the makers of Fritos, Doritos, Ruffles, and other brands of chips, is owned by the same company that makes Pepsi. This makes sense when you think about the fact that most people want something cold to drink when eating chips.

Frito-Lay's Doritos are primarily directed at teenagers. Although more male teens buy chips than female teens do, females are still considered an important part of the market. Doritos ads have appeared for years during the Super Bowl, but in 2002, Frito-Lay discontinued the ads. The company's research showed that many teens now view the Internet as more important to them than television, so Frito-Lay has tripled the amount of money it spends advertising on the Internet.

2. Do you think it was a good idea for Frito-Lay to discontinue its Doritos advertisements on the Super Bowl and shift the money to Internet advertising? Why or why not?

Go to frito-lay.com and find out how many flavors and brands of chips the company makes. For Frito-Lay to continue to grow as a company, it is always looking for new chip products. Before launching a new type of chip, Frito-Lay does lots of test marketing to see what flavor and style of chip gets the best results.

Imagine that Frito-Lay is going to introduce a new type of chip. Since teenagers are the company's target demographic, Frito-Lay asks you to survey students in your school and find out what the new flavor and style of chip should be.

It will probably be easier to do this as a group project.

Before you begin, consider the following questions on page 44.

(continued)

Dealing with the Munchies -

What kind of questions are you going to ask?

- Open-ended questions allow the students who respond to the survey to express their own feelings and opinions about a new chip. However, open-ended questions presume that people actually have feelings and opinions on the subject, and that they can express them in words. This is not always the case. After asking all your respondents an open-ended question, you need to sit down and see what the most common responses are. In other words, if you asked 100 people what new kind of chip they wanted, and 3 said an extra salty chip, and 45 said they would like a sweet chip with cinnamon on it, which type of chip would you recommend?

- Close-ended questions can be answered with "yes" or "no." There can be more than two choices, but the choices are always provided by the person asking the questions. The respondent then chooses his or her answer from those choices. The problem here is that you may not be giving the respondent a chance to tell what he or she really wants or does not want, since you are creating the answers for him or her. To tabulate close-ended questions, you simply count the number of people who responded to each given choice of answers.

- Likert scale questions use a numbered scale, such as from 1 to 5, or from 1 to 10. For example, a question that asked about how spicy somebody wanted a new chip to be could use 1 for "not spicy at all" to 10 for "so spicy it's scary." The advantage of a Likert scale is that it allows you to arrive at a numerical average. ("Of 100 people surveyed, they said they liked a spiciness level of 6.3 on a 10-point scale.") The problem with this type of question is the same as with other close-ended questions—you are limiting the types of responses a person can give you.

How many questions are you going to ask? Too many will bore your respondents after a while. Too few might mean you do not ask all the questions you should.

How many people are you going to ask? Since this is not a professional survey, you will not have the opportunity to ask nearly as many people as Frito-Lay would in a real survey, which might include hundreds of people in different parts of the country.

Finally, what are the questions you are going to ask? List them, making certain that you explain what type of question each question is—open-ended, close-ended, Likert scale. Use another sheet of paper for your list.

After you design your survey, administer your survey at your school. Tabulate your results and discuss them with classmates.

Shaving and Experiential Marketing - - - - - - - - - - - - - - - - - -

MARKETING RESEARCH has shown that most American females view shaving their legs and underarms as a necessary but unpleasant routine. This is partly due to females' perception that having hair on their legs and underarms is not feminine. Men, however, have been found to actually enjoy shaving, in part because having facial hair is a sign of masculinity. For men, shaving seems to be a ritual of manhood rather than a chore. In this view, shaving proves that a man is indeed a man, and good grooming proves that he is a respectable man.

As a result of these findings, manufacturers of shaving products offer their products to men as much more than a blade and some soap. Instead, ads for men's shaving products emphasize that those products allow men to enjoy the experience of being a man. This is called **experiential marketing.** In this kind of marketing, the advertiser emphasizes the experience a consumer will have with a product, rather than the product itself.

1. Find three print or television ads directed toward males that emphasize their products as part of a celebrated male ritual. Since we have already discussed beer, trucks, and shaving, find examples using other products. List the three products in the chart. Then, list the words or images used in the ads, and describe how those words or images portray a celebration of manliness. Use another sheet of paper, if necessary.

Product	Key words/images	How manly?

Many other products rely on experiential marketing. Remember the Pepsi ad that had Faith Hill singing a song about the "Joy of Cola"? Nothing was said about the product itself. The message of the advertisement was that the consumer's act of drinking Pepsi is a fun experience.

2. Find three ads for products that rely on experiential marketing that are directed at both men and women. In the chart below, list the three products. Then list the words or images used in the ads. Finally, describe how those words or images emphasize the user's experience with the product rather than something about the product itself. Use another sheet of paper, if necessary.

Product	Key words/images	How emphasize experience?

The objectives of this unit are to help students

- understand how visual and auditory imagery are constructed and manipulated in order to engage consumers
- develop awareness of the use of a boycott as a social and an economic strategy
- use the Internet to research business transactions
- understand how advertisers use marketing research to refine their messages

MANY OF THOSE who teach today comment on what is seen as the increasing diminution of students' attention spans and the perception that students are becoming increasingly visual learners. (It can be argued that today these characteristics describe the American public in general.) This unit discusses how television and radio advertising have contributed to these phenomena. Ironically, television and radio advertisers actively search for ways to battle these phenomena in their efforts to attract the American public's attention.

In this Unit . . .

The Hard Cut allows students to investigate the ways in which television advertisers attract and maintain consumers' attention through editing techniques and construction of visual imagery.

Lights! Cameras! Tunes! has students investigate the role of music in television and radio advertising.

Television Commercials and Setting provides students with a method of analyzing how the setting of commercials can evoke certain attitudes among consumers.

MTV and You introduces students to the practice of cool hunting. Students will discover how a television network completely focused on teen viewers develops its programming, as well as the role marketing plays in MTV programming.

The Boycott has students evaluate the effectiveness and the ethical aspects of boycotts by advocacy groups against television advertisers.

Product Placement and Positive Attitudes introduces students to the subtle and effective use of product placement within television programs.

Televised Sports and Advertising requires students to do some basic Internet research, as they search for information about the money advertisers pay for naming rights on stadiums and arenas. Students also evaluate the effectiveness of the millions of dollars spent on these naming rights.

Radio and Demographics asks students to distinguish the musical tastes of different age groups and different genders, and requires them to predict what types of products will be directed to these different groups. Students check their predictions empirically.

COMMERCIAL RADIO stations began broadcasting in the United States in the 1920s. Commercial television stations began broadcasting in the 1940s. By "commercial," we mean radio and television stations that rely on advertisers to make a profit. These stations must pay their employees, pay for their electronic equipment, pay for their buildings, and pay for the programming they broadcast, while not charging listeners for the entertainment provided.

Radio and television broadcasters attempt to appeal to certain demographic audiences. Once an audience has been gathered, salespeople for the broadcaster seek advertisers who are interested in advertising to that station's audience. Modern television advertising shows a trend toward shorter advertisements, with lots of **hard cuts** (rapid shifting from one image to another) and music. In general, the pacing of television advertising has continually sped up over the past forty years. Old television and radio advertisements would sometimes last a minute or more; now, there are many advertisements that last only ten seconds.

> **"Advertisers spent $54.4 billion on television advertising in 2001."**

Radio Advertising

Radio advertising is usually done by local businesses, such as stores, restaurants, and clubs, although some national advertisers also run advertisements on radio. Radio advertising is very inexpensive compared to other media such as television. This is because the cost of making a radio advertisement is low. All a radio advertisement needs is one or two voices, maybe with some sound effects or music. The price charged by radio stations to run an advertisement is also relatively low. Because the advertisements are inexpensive, those who advertise on radio can afford to emphasize frequency—one may hear many advertisements for the same advertiser, or may hear the same advertisement repeatedly.

This emphasis on frequency can also be explained by the fact that many of us pay very little attention to what is being said on the radio. Advertisers know this, so they often rely on repetition. Although one or two advertisements for a particular product may not get our attention, hearing advertisements for the same product dozens of times over the course of a week helps get the advertiser's message across.

Many people listen to the radio in their cars, on the way to and from work or school. The highest radio listenership occurs during so-called "drive time"—during the morning and evening rush hours (7–9 A.M., 4–6 P.M.). Many advertisements try to appeal to impulsive decisions by people who are on the road—for example, for a fast food restaurant, a coffee place, a convenience store, and so on.

Differentiating Radio Stations

During the early years of radio, each radio station tried to aim itself at all listeners. With the introduction of television in the late 1940s, radio stations changed their approach. Today, different radio stations appeal to different demographic groups, in order to deliver particular audiences to advertisers. As a result, we have radio stations with music formats such as "smooth jazz," "album-oriented rock," "soft adult contemporary," "hot adult contemporary," "alternative rock," "rhythmic pop," and "classic rock."

There are over 4,700 commercial radio stations on the AM band and over 6,000 stations on the FM band in the United States. The great majority of these radio stations rely on advertising for their income. In 2001, American radio station owners received almost $17.9 billion from advertisers.

Television Advertising

There are over 1,300 commercial broadcast television stations in the United States, in addition to numerous cable channels. Just as most radio stations do, most television stations (with the exception of premium channels, such as HBO, and pay-per-view) rely on advertising to make a profit. Television rates vary greatly, depending on the size of the audience watching a particular program at a particular time. For example, a thirty-second advertisement on a local television station in a small town might cost the advertiser only a few hundred dollars. But consider that a thirty-second advertisement on the Fox network's *The Simpsons* costs over $250,000, and Fox charged $1.9 million for each thirty-second advertisement during the 2002 Super Bowl. Altogether, advertisers spent $54.4 billion on television advertising in 2001.

Television and Radio Advertising

The Hard Cut -

IN ADDITION TO the money spent to obtain commercial time on television stations, advertisers spend many millions of dollars producing the commercials that they will broadcast. Many ads today contain attention-getting special effects. These include computer-generated imagery and animation, unusual camera angles, and lots of hard cuts. A hard cut occurs when the televised image or scene on the screen abruptly changes to another, possibly very different, image.

To enhance the effect of hard cuts, there are also more images or scenes being shown in the typical television ad than was the case in the past. A thirty-second television ad twenty years ago may have had only one or two cuts. Today, a thirty-second ad may have dozens of hard cuts.

Watch five thirty-second television advertisements for different types of products. Write the number of cuts in the chart. (You may find this easier to do with the sound turned down.) Record your answers below. Use another sheet of paper, if necessary.

1. Total the number of cuts you counted for each advertisement.

Product	Number of cuts

2. Now calculate the average number of cuts for the five advertisements you measured.

3. Why do you think television advertisements have so many hard cuts?

4. Ask an older adult how she or he feels about these types of ads. Are these types of ads exciting or confusing to that person?

5. Ask that older adult why she or he feels this way.

Lights! Cameras! Tunes! -

IN THE 1950S AND 1960S, radio and television ads often relied on **jingles.** Jingles are short songs especially written for an ad, which usually name the product in the song and contain lyrics about the value of that product. Jingles are relatively inexpensive and are still used in many ads today, but advertisers have begun to rely more heavily on popular songs that have previously been performed by well-known artists. For example, Microsoft paid the Rolling Stones $12 million to use their song "Start Me Up" when the company introduced Windows 95. The legal rights to many old Beatles songs were purchased in 1985 by Michael Jackson. Jackson angered some of the former Beatles by allowing several advertisers to use some of the songs in television advertisements, including the song "Revolution" in ads for Nike shoes. Many current musicians, such as Lenny Kravitz, Moby, and G. Love and Special Sauce, have had thier music used in advertisements.

Record your answers below. Use another sheet of paper, if necessary.

1. In the chart, list three advertisers that use jingles in television or radio advertisements. Then write whether you think the jingle helps sell the product or not. Finally, explain your opinion.

Advertiser	Is jingle effective?	Explain

2. In the chart, list three advertisers that use popular songs in television or radio ads. Then list the song each advertiser uses. Next, write whether the song is effective in selling the product or not. Finally, explain your opinion.

Advertiser	Song	Effective?	Explain

3. Why do you think that advertisers are willing to pay much more money to use popular songs in their ads, instead of paying much less money for jingles?

4. Why is this a good idea or a bad idea on the part of advertisers?

Television Commercials and Setting - - - - - - - - - - - - - - - - -

THE LOCATION of where the activity occurs in a television commercial is called the setting. For example, the setting for a food product may be the kitchen where it is prepared, the dining room where it is eaten, the store where it is purchased, or the farm where it is grown. The people who produce television ads pay a lot of attention to setting because television commercials rely on visual images to sell the product. Sometimes the settings are typical—the place where one would expect the product to be used. Sometimes the settings are atypical—unusual settings chosen to get attention, or to create a mood about the product.

1. Watch three television advertisements for cars and other vehicles. Make sure that at least one of the advertisements is for a sports utility vehicle (SUV) or a truck. Fill in the chart. Use another sheet of paper, if necessary.

   List the brand of each advertised vehicle.

   Then list the setting of each advertisement—in the city, the suburbs, or the countryside. Then explain why you think each setting was chosen.

   Next, write whether the vehicle looks like it's going fast or slow.

   In the next column, write whether you can hear the noise the car makes, or whether there is music or talking instead.

   Next, if there is music, is there a relationship between the music and the speed of the vehicle? Write *yes* or *no* and explain.

   Finally, write what the announcer tells you about each vehicle.

Vehicle name	Setting	Why this setting?	Fast or slow?	Sound	Music related to speed?	Announcer's words

(continued)

Activity 3 *(continued)*

Television Commercials and Setting - - - - - - - - - - - - - - - - -

Many advertisers today emphasize experiential marketing. This means that they don't focus on the product being sold, but on how the product (supposedly) can make the consumer feel.

2. Is the information given about the vehicles in the ads you viewed mostly facts about the car—price, engine size, number of passengers—or about attitude? Explain.

3. Do you think that information given about each vehicle is important to the type of person who would buy that vehicle? Explain.

4. Let's look at the use of mood in ads. Watch three television ads for long-distance telephone service or for cell phone service. (Try watching with the sound turned down.) Describe the faces of the people shown in the ad.

   Do people always feel this way when using long distance service or a cell phone?

   Why are people shown this way?

Most soft drink ads do not talk about how the product tastes. Many people say that these ads are really trying to sell a positive attitude about the product, conveying that how cool a product is to drink is more important than how it tastes.

5. Do you agree or disagree with this statement? Why?

MTV and You -

YOU ARE A MEMBER of the key demographic group that MTV works hard to appeal to. MTV uses some of its employees to do cool hunting. Cool hunters go out into different communities to talk to teenagers about what's cool right now and what's not. Using this research, MTV tries to create programs that you will think are cool, so that you and your friends will watch them. MTV shares some of the information it finds with the companies that advertise on MTV so that advertisers can make commercials that are also cool.

Get a stopwatch, such as the stopwatch feature on many wristwatches. A kitchen timer will work, too. Watch MTV for an hour.

- Count how many advertisements you see during that hour (count music videos, if any, as advertisements for record companies). Write that number down.

- Also count how many products, if any, are identified by name during the programs, as opposed to the advertisements (this includes the name of a new CD, a new video, a new movie). Write that number down.

- How many minutes of the hour were devoted to various forms of advertising activity, including commercials and the naming of products during the programs?

- Do the math—what percentage of the hour was devoted to various forms of advertising activity?

- Can commercials be cool?

- Why or why not?

- Are there some ads that you know are ads that you actually enjoy watching? Explain.

The Boycott -

A BOYCOTT MEANS to refuse to do business with a company because it is believed to have done something wrong, or is currently doing something wrong. The goal of a boycott is to either punish a business for what it has done wrong, or to put pressure on that business to change its practices.

Sometimes different groups of people take up a boycott, or at least threaten one, that is directed toward television advertisers. These groups may be angry at the advertiser itself, perhaps for showing an advertisement that is considered insulting or shocking to some people. Sometimes these groups are upset at the television shows during which an advertiser runs its commercials. The strategy is, if advertisers know that some people will not buy products advertised during certain television shows, then the advertisers will put pressure on the television network to change the show, or the advertisers will take their business elsewhere.

For example, in April 2001, the *Dr. Laura* show was cancelled due to a successful boycott. Dr. Laura Schlessinger had a television program that talked about relationships. She was an outspoken critic of homosexuality. Gay and lesbian groups organized a boycott of the advertisers who ran ads during the program. Some advertisers refused to advertise during the program. The television stations that broadcast the program began to lose money and chose to stop showing it.

Years before, the American Family Association (AFA) pressured advertisers to stop running commercials during *Saturday Night Live.* The AFA argued that the show had too much sexual content and made fun of Christian beliefs. More recently, the AFA threatened a boycott of advertisers whose commercials aired during ABC's *Ellen,* when the show's star, Ellen DeGeneres, announced that she is a lesbian.

Not all television advertiser boycotts deal with sexual issues. For example, the National Association for the Advancement of Colored People (an organization of African Americans), the Media Action Network for Asian Americans, the National Hispanic Foundation for the Arts, and other groups were angered when the 1999 television season introduced twenty-six new shows, none of which had a person of color in a leading role. After the groups threatened a boycott of network television, ABC, CBS, NBC, and Fox all agreed to create more ethnic diversity on their programs. Some Italian-American groups have objected to the frequent representation of Italian Americans as members of organized crime. Other boycotts have been directed at advertisers for airing advertisements that were seen as racially insensitive.

One of the more interesting boycotts occurred after a "Sexy Gothic Makeovers" segment on the *Jenny Jones Show.* Boycott organizers believed that the show mistreated members of the Goth community.

(continued)

The Boycott -

Some people argue that most advertising is a "one-way street" because advertisers tell us what they want to, but consumers usually do not have the chance to respond. These people say that regardless of the message (in this case, the reason for the boycott), it is important that people are allowed to organize a boycott, even if you personally disagree with the particular message.

1. Do you believe a boycott of advertisers is a good way to make television companies more respectful of a certain group of people? Explain.

Sometimes, the advertiser itself is the target of a boycott. For example, an advertisement for the Toyota RAV 4 portrayed an African-American man in a manner that some African-American groups found insulting. The threatened boycott caused Toyota to discontinue the advertisement and publicly apologize.

2. Do you believe a boycott of an advertiser is a good way to make that advertiser more respectful of a certain group of people? Explain.

Some people argue that a boycott of television programs or advertisers is a form of censorship.

3. Do you agree? Explain.

Product Placement and Positive Attitudes - - - - - - - - - - - -

ADVERTISERS ARE CONCERNED that many of us watch television with a remote control in our hand. They worry that when ads come on, we switch channels. As a result, advertisers are putting more attention into product placement. Advertisers pay the producers of television programs to show the characters on those programs using the advertisers' products. The character who uses the product is one that viewers are supposed to like. In most cases, you will not see a bad guy use the "placed" product! Some products placed in programs include Diet Coke and Heinz ketchup.

Record your answers below. Use another sheet of paper, if necessary.

1. If you were an advertiser, would you think that product placement is a good idea or a bad idea? Why?

2. In the chart, list three programs that are currently shown on television. Then list an existing product (by brand, like "Coke" or by product type, like "soft drink") that would be a good product to place on the program. Finally, explain why you think that program would be a good one for placing that product.

Program title	Product name/type	Why good for placement?

3. As a consumer, do you think product placement is a good idea or a bad idea? Why?

The federal government is also involved in product placement—sort of. In 1997, Congress decided to spend federal money to insert antidrug-abuse messages in such programs as *ER*, *Beverly Hills 90210*, *Chicago Hope*, *The Drew Carey Show*, and *7th Heaven*. Congress agreed to spend $1 billion over five years, on the condition that the networks give the government a significant discount on advertising prices.

4. Do you think using taxpayers' money to have fictional television characters talk against drug abuse is a good idea or a bad idea? Why?

In most product placement, advertisers are trying to sell a product. In the government's antidrug-abuse campaign, the government is trying to sell an idea or an attitude.

5. What do you think is harder to sell, a product or an attitude? Why?

Televised Sports and Advertising ------------------

MANY OF THE sporting events on television have a corporate sponsor. For example, professional golf tournaments include the Sony Open and the Kraft Nabisco Championship. College bowl games are frequently named after companies, such as the Nokia Sugar Bowl. The arenas and stadiums in which televised games are played usually have dozens of ads located throughout the building. In fact, although cigarette companies are not allowed to advertise on television, until recently ads for cigarettes were visible inside sports arenas and stadiums during televised games. (This practice has since been discontinued, as discussed in Unit 2.)

Many stadiums and arenas in which professional sports teams play also have companies' names in their titles. This is not because those companies own those stadiums and arenas. Instead, the owners sell the "naming rights" to those buildings. Naming rights are considered a part of a company's advertising, and many companies are willing to spend millions for that right.

Record your answers here and on page 59. Use another sheet of paper, if necessary.

1. List and describe three benefits that a company receives by paying for the naming rights on stadiums and arenas.

2. Do you believe these reasons justify spending millions of dollars? Explain.

Sometimes, the arena or stadium that has its naming rights sold to a private company is actually owned by the public. In other words, the community's taxpayers paid to build the building, but a private company paid to have its name put on that building.

3. Do you think this is a good idea or a bad idea? Why?

Sometimes the money that is paid to name a public stadium goes to the people who own the team instead of to the community that owns the stadium. This practice is defended by some people, who say that the owner of the team can use the money to get better players.

4. Do you think this is a good idea or a bad idea? Why?

(continued)

Televised Sports and Advertising - - - - - - - - - - - - - - - - - - -

In 1999, the energy company Enron agreed to pay $100 million over 30 years for the naming rights for the Houston Astros' new baseball stadium. Two years later, Enron became widely known for a huge financial scandal. The company went bankrupt, thousands of people lost their jobs, and government authorities began investigating possible criminal activity.

5. If you were the owner of the Houston Astros, what would you do in this situation? Why?

The rest of this activity requires some Internet research.

6. Find out on the Internet what the owner of the Astros did.

7. Do you think he made the right decision? Explain.

Research the names of three stadiums or arenas near you where professional sports teams play.

8. Write the name of those three stadiums or arenas.

9. For each stadium named after a company, find out how much those companies paid for the naming rights and how long the contract is for.

Radio and Demographics -

TELEVISION BROADCASTERS and radio broadcasters both try to develop an audience for their stations through programming. Television broadcasters choose programs that will attract a certain type of audience. For example, football games will attract a mostly male audience. Soap operas will attract mostly female viewers. Cartoons are aimed at young children. Radio broadcasters develop their audiences through the type of music they play. Oldies stations are aimed at older adults, stations that play lots of rap and hip-hop are aimed at teens, heavy metal appeals more to males than to females, and so on.

Use the chart below to note information, make predictions, and draw conclusions about five local radio stations.

First, list five local stations. Include your favorite station and the preferred station of an older adult in your household. Then write what age group you think the station tries to reach. Use the following categories: 12–18, 18–24, 18–34, 34–45, 45 and older. Next, write which gender the station appeals to—or both. Then list the types of advertisers you think would advertise there. Finally, listen to each of the five stations for a few minutes, until you've heard several advertisements on each station. Were you right or wrong about the types of advertisers that you thought would advertise on that station? Write the names of the advertisers in the chart.

Radio station	Age group	Gender	Who I think would advertise here	Who does advertise here

This exercise is exactly what radio stations try to do—create a "sound" that attracts a particular type of listener and find advertisers who want to appeal to that type of listener.

The objectives of this unit are to help students

- identify the persuasive and attention-getting techniques employed in print advertising
- understand demographic and psychographic differences in American society
- evaluate the arguments of those who want to regulate certain forms of advertising and those who do not
- develop a process for decision making that requires evaluating information and identifying what additional information is needed before making an informed decision

PRINT ADVERTISING is probably the easiest form of advertising to study in a classroom setting. It is recommended that students bring to class some of their own favorite magazines as well as local newspapers. It is also easy to obtain magazines that pertain to very specific interests and activities, such as weddings, various hobbies and occupations, and so on.

Depending on where your school is located, your students may or may not have been exposed to a significant number of billboards and transit advertising on taxis and buses. The activities that discuss outdoor advertising do not require the student to have significant exposure to outdoor advertising.

In this Unit . . .

What Catches Your Eye? requires students to select the three most attention-getting advertisements in a magazine and analyze the visual and thematic aspects of each advertisement.

Something for Everybody helps students to distinguish between advertisements for low-involvement items (items that usually require little thought before buying) and advertisements for high-involvement items that require more thought.

Different Magazines, Different Advertisements has students assess demographic and psychographic differences among different magazines.

Bad Billboards in the 'Hood? asks students to evaluate the impact of tobacco and alcohol advertising in disadvantaged neighborhoods. This exercise also asks students to evaluate the role of government in regulating advertising.

Bad Billboards Everywhere? introduces students to the arguments made by groups that oppose billboards along roadways and by groups that support billboards. Students must then identify and summarize the key points of each argument and explain which side they find more persuasive.

Newspapers versus Magazines: You Decide has students simulate one of the frequent decisions made by advertising agencies regarding which medium to purchase advertising in, and why. Students are asked to compare the relative advantages and disadvantages of two competing media, and are then asked to identify what additional information they would need before making an informed decision.

Ad Buzz

PRINT ADVERTISING can (but does not always) provide more information than most other advertising formats. Print advertising is static—it does not move. People (and other animals) are attracted to movement, so print advertising uses various techniques to get our attention. For example, the ads on the right page (called the *recto* side in the advertising business) of a newspaper or magazine usually cost more than the same-size ad on the left (*verso*) side. This is because readers of English use the Roman alphabet (as compared to the Arabic or Japanese alphabets, for example). Since our written words move from left to right, our eyes naturally move toward the right when we read a newspaper or a magazine. Similarly, our eye usually will take us to the top left side of the page and continue down to the bottom right side of the page. As a result, most newspaper and magazine ads are loosely arranged in the form of the letter Z, taking our eyes across the information the advertiser wants us exposed to.

> **"About 60% of a typical newspaper is devoted to advertising."**

Beauty for the Eye of the Beholder

Ads in magazines rely on color photography to get our attention. The objects in the photographs are carefully arranged to be as eye-catching as possible. Photographs of fashion models in ads for personal care products are almost always airbrushed to remove any blemishes. Today, more and more photographs are also digitally altered—edited by the photographer to put in or take out anything he or she decides. (Blemishes can be removed, color of hair and eyes changed, and fullness added to lips.) Tattoos, so popular today, can be added, removed, or changed, too.

About 60% of a typical newspaper is devoted to advertising. Newspapers usually contain more ads for local stores, services, and so on than magazines do. Some of this advertising is designed by the advertiser itself, as opposed to an advertising agency. As a result, some of the newspaper advertising may be less sophisticated than magazine advertising, since advertising agencies usually create magazine advertising.

Who's Looking?

Different readers favor different sections of the newspaper. Ads aimed primarily at men often appear in the sports section; advertisements aimed primarily at women often appear in the living, lifestyle, or home section.

Billboards

Billboards—large ads on frames by the side of roadways—are another form of print advertising. In some ways, billboards require advertisers to use the opposite approach of that used in other print advertising. Magazine and newspaper ads can provide a lot of information. Billboards have to get their message across quickly. Billboards are typically along major roadways, designed to get the attention of motorists and their passengers. The billboard industry says that a billboard ad, to be effective, must communicate its information within six to ten seconds. Thus, billboard advertising pays careful attention to short messages, attractive colors, easy-to-read lettering, and photographs or drawings that get the message across quickly to the consumer.

What Catches Your Eye? -

Look at all the advertisements in one magazine. Find the three advertisements that get your attention the most, cut them out, and attach them to this page.

1. For each advertisement, explain why it caught your attention.
   Ad 1:

   Ad 2:

   Ad 3:

2. For each advertisement, describe the visual composition of the advertisement. Were the colors used particularly attention-getting, either because they were unusual or because they were especially pretty or ugly? Explain.
   Ad 1:

   Ad 2:

   Ad 3:

   Was the type of lettering attention-getting? Explain.
   Ad 1:

   Ad 2:

   Ad 3:

   Was the way the pictures, drawings, and words were arranged on the page attention-getting? Explain.
   Ad 1:

   Ad 2:

   Ad 3:

(continued)

What Catches Your Eye? -

3. For each advertisement, describe the theme or subject of the advertisement:

   Ad 1:

   Ad 2:

   Ad 3:

   Was the theme unusual for the type of product being advertised? (For example, using a photograph of a kid on a skateboard to sell a computer—most people would not automatically connect the two together.) Explain.

   Ad 1:

   Ad 2:

   Ad 3:

4. Was the language used in the wording attention-getting? Explain.

   Ad 1:

   Ad 2:

   Ad 3:

5. Did each advertisement suggest a certain attitude that the advertiser has, or that the consumer has? Explain.

   Ad 1:

   Ad 2:

   Ad 3:

Something for Everybody -

THERE ARE OVER 17,000 different magazines in the United States. Most magazines contain both editorial and advertising content. (Editorial content means the articles or stories put in by the writers and editors.) In 2001, the ratio for consumer magazines was 45% advertising, 55% editorial. This means there are hundreds of millions of pages of magazine ads each year.

Very few magazines today are directed at the general population. Instead, magazines focus on particular demographic and psychographic groups. For instance, women's fashion magazines are aimed at different age groups; *Vogue* is intended for readers older than the average reader of *Seventeen.* Some women's fashion magazines are aimed at women from minority groups. Many magazines are directed at specific interests or hobbies—for example, magazines aimed at dog owners, cat owners, people who like to cook, musicians, and so on. The intention behind this specialization is to deliver a particular type of reader to the advertiser.

1. Go to a library, a bookstore, or any other store that has a large number of magazines. Look through three magazines that you've never read before. Use the chart below to record information about these magazines.

    First, write the title of each magazine.

    Then write the type of reader you think the magazine is intended for. Include both demographic and psychographic information.

    Finally, list the clues that led you to determine the intended audience.

Magazine	Type of reader	Clues

2. What was more helpful when trying to determine the type of reader of each magazine—the editorial content or the advertising? Explain.

Different Magazines, Different Advertisements ------

SOME ADVERTISED PRODUCTS are low-involvement items that one may use without much thought. For example, when was the last time you thought about a soft drink? High-involvement items are often more expensive or require significant emotional investment. For example, if you were going to buy a car, are you likely to buy the first one you see?

Look at ads in a business magazine such as *Fortune, Forbes, Business Week,* or the *Economist.* Now look at ads in fashion magazines such as *Glamour* or *GQ,* and ads in sports and entertainment magazines such as *Sports Illustrated* and *Spin.*

1. How do ads in business magazines differ from ads in fashion, sports, and entertainment magazines?

2. Which magazines' ads give the reader the most information?

3. How do these ads provide more information?

4. Why do you think more information is provided in ads in some types of magazines, and less information is provided in other types of magazines?

Bad Billboards in the 'Hood? -

A SURVEY IN St. Louis, Missouri, found twice as many billboards in black neighborhoods as in white neighborhoods. Almost 60% of the billboards in the black neighborhoods advertised alcoholic beverages and cigarettes. In another study in Philadelphia, Pennsylvania, 60 of the 73 billboards in a 19-block area were found to advertise cigarettes or alcohol. In Baltimore, Maryland, a study found that most of the billboards in that city were in poor black neighborhoods, and most of the billboards in those neighborhoods advertised alcohol or tobacco products.[1]

A few people in predominately black neighborhoods have taken it upon themselves to paint over billboards advertising alcohol and tobacco products. These people point to the fact that the management of nearly all American producers of alcohol and tobacco are white. The claim by those who paint over the billboards is that white people working for rich companies are preying on black people, especially black people in poorer neighborhoods. In other words, the management of these companies put their billboards in black neighborhoods when they wouldn't have them in their own. They do this because of the health risks of alcohol and tobacco.

1. Do you agree or disagree with those people who want to keep billboards for alcohol and tobacco products out of some neighborhoods? Explain.

Some people believe that companies that sell alcohol and tobacco products should be very careful about how they advertise. These people also believe that if the companies are not careful enough, then the government should be able to regulate what alcohol and tobacco companies can or cannot say in their advertisements. Other people believe that alcohol and tobacco companies should be able to do what they want and let people make up their own minds about whether or not to buy alcohol or tobacco.

2. Which side do you believe makes the best argument? Explain.

---

[1] These statistics were gathered by Vernellia R. Randall, Professor of Law at the University of Dayton.

Bad Billboards Everywhere? -

THE WORD *aesthetics* relates to a perception of beauty. Some people believe that billboards, which are usually along roadways, hurt the aesthetics of many roadways that pass through areas of natural beauty, such as countrysides and seasides. Even in cities, these people argue, the billboards only make a less-than-beautiful situation worse. People who are opposed to billboards also claim that the billboards create traffic safety hazards. After all, most billboards are along roadways and are designed to get people's attention. This means they distract drivers, causing unsafe driving conditions.

Those who defend billboards (including advertisers and companies that own billboards) point to the First Amendment of the U.S Constitution, which guarantees freedom of speech. Those who oppose billboards remind us that freedom of speech has never been interpreted as the freedom to say anything that anybody wants to say. For example, as U.S. Supreme Court Justice Oliver Wendell Holmes, Jr., once said, freedom of speech does not give us the right to yell "fire" in a crowded movie theater when there is not a fire, since that could create a dangerous situation in which panicky people could be trampled to death.

People who defend billboards also argue that because billboards help create more business for advertisers, billboards help the economy. The economic benefits include providing jobs for not only the billboard companies' employees, but also for the employees of the companies that advertise on billboards. Defenders of billboards also point out that the land on which billboards are placed is usually owned by someone other than the billboard company. Defenders of billboards argue that these landowners are legally entitled to use their property in a reasonable manner, including earning income by renting space to the billboard companies.

1. List the arguments given in favor of prohibiting billboards.

2. List the arguments given in favor of protecting billboards.

(continued)

Bad Billboards Everywhere? -----------------------

3. Which side are you on in this situation? Why?

Several U.S. Supreme Court cases have said that commercial speech (which includes advertising) is not protected by the First Amendment to the same degree that personal speech is. For example, if you want to encourage other people to vote for somebody you like, or if you want to encourage people to go to a particular church or temple, this type of speech is highly protected and very hard for the government to interfere with. If, however, you own a business and you want to encourage people to buy things from you, this type of speech is viewed by the courts as less important, so it is not as protected. This means the government may be able to place restrictions on advertising by businesses, although the government may not similarly restrict a person's political or religious speech (grouped together under the term "ideological speech").

4. Do you agree with the U.S. Supreme Court—that commercial speech is not as important as ideological speech? Explain.

Newspapers versus Magazines: You Decide - - - - - - - - - - -

ABOUT ONE-HALF to two-thirds of American adults read daily newspapers. The older a person is, the more likely it is that she or he reads a daily newspaper. About 72% of people age 65 and older read a newspaper each day, while about 40% of people between the ages of 18 and 24 read a newspaper each day. The more educated a person is, the more likely she or he is to read a newspaper. Similarly, the more money a person makes, the more likely she or he is to read a newspaper. In general, though, most daily newspapers are directed at just about everybody in that newspaper's community who can read. Many newspaper ads are for local advertisers, but newspapers also contain ads for national companies.

Imagine that you work for a chewing gum company that sells its chewing gum products through-out the United States. You are trying to decide if you should advertise in local newspapers or national magazines. Newspaper ads are usually less expensive than magazine ads. So if you choose to run your ads in newspapers, you will be able to advertise in more newspapers than magazines. We will presume that if you advertise in local newspapers, you will advertise in the 100 largest cities in the country. If you advertise in magazines, you will choose from 20 of the 100 most popular magazines. Some things to consider when making your decision include

- Do you want to use color in your advertising (color is common in most magazines, and rare for advertising in most newspapers)?
- Who will see your ads in newspapers? Who will see your ads in magazines?
- Do you want to advertise in 100 newspapers that are read by various types of people, or do you want to advertise in 20 magazines that you will select based on the certain types of people who read those magazines?

1. List three advantages of advertising chewing gum in newspapers instead of in magazines.

2. List three disadvantages of advertising chewing gum in newspapers instead of in magazines.

(continued)

Newspapers versus Magazines: You Decide - - - - - - - - - - -

3. List three advantages of advertising chewing gum in magazines instead of in newspapers.

4. List three disadvantages of advertising chewing gum in magazines instead of in newspapers.

5. List three facts that you would want to know about the demographics of chewing gum consumers before making a decision about whether to advertise in newspapers or in magazines. Tell why you would want each piece of information.

The objectives of this unit are to help students

- understand the commercial nature of the Internet
- scrutinize the motives and techniques of firms that engage in stealth marketing
- analyze the tension between interstate commerce and individual privacy
- rely on their own creativity and imagination in generating new ideas for the relatively new medium of the Internet

THE INTERACTIVITY of the Internet offers potential benefits to both advertisers and consumers. Interactivity allows advertisers to tailor their messages to individual web users, and to gather often instantaneous feedback about what types of advertising do and do not work. Consumers can benefit from two-way communication with advertisers, but significant privacy issues also arise. Students tend to have much less concern for privacy than do older adults. Part of this may simply be a generational difference in an American society that is increasingly information-driven. Senior citizens generally have a greater concern for privacy than do middle-aged adults, who usually have a greater concern for privacy than do teenagers. Students often are flattered that advertisers want to know what they think. The challenge for the teacher in this unit is to help the students understand the consequences of providing information about themselves to advertisers.

In this Unit . . .

Portal: The Fancy Word for a Start Page explains the advertising functions of start pages on the Internet.

gURL.Com: It Says It's for Girls. Is It by Girls? has students investigate a commercial web site that aggressively collects information about consumers while using stealth marketing techniques.

A Portal for Teens, by Teens may be best undertaken as a group project. This activity allows students to be creative as they undertake the design of their own start page for teens.

And They're Just Getting Started! requires students to count the number of advertisements they encounter in a typical surfing session—this activity is available to both regular visitors to the Internet and to novices.

Dot Com = Dot Bomb? has students evaluate the reasons why many Internet-related firms have had disappointing financial results thus far, and requires students to use imagination and creativity to generate successful methods of engaging consumers.

THE WORD "Internet" was first used in 1982. But the history of the Internet actually begins in the 1960s, as organizations involved in national defense began to design new ways of connecting their computers so that these different agencies could "talk" to each other. In 1991, the World Wide Web was introduced. Mosaic, the first graphics-based web browser, followed in 1993. Mosaic was important because it allowed users to see pictures and photographs instead of just words. Before Mosaic, most Internet communication was basically like e-mail.

On-line advertising first became a widespread practice around 1996. Perhaps the reason that commercial advertisers became most excited about the Internet is that it allows interactivity. This means that instead of advertising being a one-way street with the information coming only from the advertiser, the Internet allows advertisers to receive communications from consumers. This is not because advertisers like you and think you're cool! Rather, interactivity allows advertisers to find out quickly which advertising messages work and which do not. Interactivity also allows advertisers to build a database about consumers, and a database allows advertisers to do data mining. For example, if a teen subscribes to a magazine, the magazine (and its advertisers) may know nothing about that subscriber except his or her name and address. Inside the magazine, the magazine might feature a contest or an opinion poll that asks the reader to go to the magazine's web site. Once there, the magazine can ask for demo-

> **"Interactivity also allows advertisers to build a database about consumers."**

graphic and psychographic information about the reader: his or her age, hobbies, likes and dislikes, and so on. Or an advertisement inside the magazine might include the advertiser's web site and encourage readers to go to that site. That advertiser's web site might ask for similar demographic and psychographic information.

Another, somewhat controversial, way that Internet sites learn about you is by use of **cookies.** Cookies are unique identifiers put on your computer by web sites when you surf the Internet. Some cookies are actually quite helpful to you, the computer user. For example, if you have a personal start page on your computer, such as "My Yahoo," the cookie tells Yahoo who you are each time you log on and presents the information that you've asked for, such as your personal horoscope, your favorite sports teams' scores, or the weather in your community. Also, when shopping at web sites that you commonly visit, the cookie keeps information about your shipping address and your credit card number, among other things. Sometimes, however, cookies are used by web sites to "spy" on you. It has been found that many web surfers freely reveal information about themselves without concern for their privacy. Advertisers that maintain web sites might create a special site that is promoted only in a particular magazine, such as *Seventeen* or *Sports Illustrated.* When surfers go to those web sites, the advertiser is then able to measure which magazine advertisements create the best response among different types of ads in different media. Most responsible web sites have a privacy policy, which can be read by visitors to those sites.

In 1998, the U.S Government's Federal Trade Commission enacted the Children's Online Privacy Protection Rule, under the direction of

Congress. This rule applies to operators of commercial web sites and on-line services directed to children under the age of 13, and to general audience web sites and on-line services that knowingly collect personal information from children under 13. Among other things, the rule requires that web sites get consent from a parent or guardian before collecting personal information from children.

Some consumers enjoy the interactivity that cookies provide—they feel that it allows advertisers to customize information to consumers' personal attitudes and habits. Others feel that interactivity is intrusive. They believe that the Internet allows advertisers to intrude in our lives, and perhaps violate our privacy.

Advertising on the Internet takes two basic forms: advertising banners and web sites maintained by an advertiser. For example, let's say you are reading a news story at a **portal** such as MSN.com. The MSN site may have a banner advertisement for Abercrombie and Fitch—even though you were not looking for information about clothing, you have now seen the advertisement. Often times, a banner advertisement is a

click-through. This means that if you click on the banner advertisement you will be led to Abercrombie and Fitch's own web site. This web site is advertised in Abercrombie and Fitch's magazine advertisements and in promotional displays in its stores. The web site allows you to do on-line shopping. It also includes music downloads, photographs of models, e-mail postcards that you can send to friends, and other items. If lots of visitors to the site click on one type of postcard, but not another, the company learns what sorts of pictures are popular with its consumers and what type of pictures are not. This is the value of interactivity to the company—it now knows what type of pictures to use in its advertising and what type to avoid.

Remember that television and radio were created as commercial media from the beginning. The entertainment and information that television and radio often provide us for free is actually paid for by advertisers. Similarly, the content provided on the Internet costs money to those who make that information and entertainment available to us. Many of the web sites that provide information and entertainment hope to make money through advertising.

Portal: The Fancy Word for a Start Page -----------

MANY INTERNET USERS have established start pages (also called home pages) where they begin their Internet surfing. Examples include My Yahoo, My Excite, and My MSN. These sites are attractive to users because they allow us to collect information that is important or interesting to us, such as local news and weather, television listings, information about favorite entertainers and sports teams, even our daily horoscope. The companies that provide these customizable start pages also gather information from cookies to present ads from companies that are seeking users' demographic and psychographic profiles. For example, a start page for a 42-year-old person might have ads for weight-loss programs (especially in early January, when lots of middle-aged people make New Year's resolutions about losing weight). A banner advertising the latest Backstreet Boys CD might appear on the start page of a teen female, while a banner advertising a WWE pay-per-view event might appear on the start page of a teen male. The companies that provide free start pages to web surfers make a profit from this service by charging the advertisers who place banners or other ads on those start pages. This is similar to radio or broadcast television—the user does not pay for the medium, the advertiser does. However, unlike radio or television, advertisers on start pages can directly measure response to their ads. This occurs when we click on a banner; something that very few (less than one percent) of us do.

Record your answers below. Use another sheet of paper, if necessary.

1. What do you think a web portal with Yahoo does with the information it learns about you when you create a start page, when you buy things at a Yahoo-sponsored site, or when you send e-mail through a Yahoo address? List everything you think that Yahoo might do with that information, and explain why you think this.

Now, go to yahoo.com, scroll to the bottom of the page, and click on "privacy policy." Read the policy.

2. Do you understand everything that Yahoo's privacy policy tells you? Explain your answer, giving examples from the privacy policy, if necessary.

After reviewing this privacy policy, do you feel comfortable that Yahoo is protecting your privacy? Explain.

gURL.Com: It Says It's for Girls. Is It by Girls? - - - - - - - - - -

STEALTH MARKETING occurs when an advertiser tries to make it look like it is not engaging in marketing activities when it actually is. *Stealth* means "sneaky." Since many consumers grow tired of advertising and since there is so much advertising around, advertisers search for sneaky methods of advertising.

Go to gURL.com. Click around the site so that you can answer the following questions.

1. List the different ways this web site tries to get information about people who visit it.

2. In the chart below, list the different types of information this web site tries to gather about people. Then write why you think the web site wants this information. If you think the web site does not really want a particular piece of information (it's just acting like it cares), explain why you believe that.

Types of information	Why?

3. Research on the web. Find who owns gURL.com. What else does that company own?

4. Describe why gURL.com is an example of stealth marketing.

A Portal for Teens, by Teens -

YOU ARE GOING TO CREATE your own start page for teens. You need to make this site interesting to both males and females. This is a good group project for males and females.

Before you begin, you need to decide on what sort of information teens are interested in that would make them want to begin a surfing session at your web site. Think about news, weather, sports, music, movies, fashion, and other types of information. Check existing portals such as Yahoo, Excite, and MSN. Try to make yours different from theirs.

1. In the space below, draw what your start page will look like.

2. Below each item on your web site, explain why you put that information there.
3. Of course, getting space on the Internet is not free. You have to pay the bills. What types of advertisers would be interested in advertising on your web site? Why?

And They're Just Getting Started! ------------------

AS MENTIONED in the Ad Buzz, the Internet became a commercial medium around 1996. In the years since, commercial web sites and on-line advertisers have multiplied rapidly. If you do not regularly surf the net, get on-line and poke around. If you regularly surf the net, get on-line and do what you normally do when you surf. During this session, carefully count the number of ads you encounter as you surf. Some ads will appear as banners, some will appear only as links, some may appear as the hated pop-ups (these are ads that pop up on your screen even when you do not click on an advertising link or banner). Count every single ad.

1. How many advertisements did you count?

2. Were you surprised? Why or why not?

3. When you normally surf, do you occasionally click on banners or advertisers' links? Why or why not? (Answer this question, if applicable.)

4. Does it bother you that there is so much advertising on the Internet? Why or why not?

Dot Com = Dot Bomb? -

SOME BUSINESS EXPERTS have said that the number one reason businesses fail is overoptimism. This means that many people start a business so confident of success that they are not careful enough in their planning of that new business. In the late 1990s, Internet businesses that were called "dot coms" were all the rage in the business world. Many people were so sure of the Internet's ability to make them rich that they borrowed and spent huge amounts of money building companies that were supposed to make money from Internet business.

One example that you may remember was Pets.com. Its advertisements were catchy, featuring a sock puppet dog that was funny and also a pretty bad singer. The company soon found, however, that consumers did not want to pay the shipping charges for heavy bags of dog food. Even though people loved the company's advertisements, Pets.com went out of business in 2000, only two years after it was founded. The company joined the growing list of dot coms that have become dot bombs.

Other companies have tried to make money by selling advertising on their sites. Remember that a magazine sets the price of its advertising based in part on how many people read that magazine. Television stations set the price of advertising based on how many people watch a particular program. Web sites that sell advertising track how many people visit that web site each day, and many web sites have thousands and thousands of viewers daily. It is one thing to see an advertisement, however, and quite another thing to buy what the advertiser is selling. While it is hard for an advertiser to know if a particular advertisement in a particular magazine is helping to sell products, an advertiser can usually tell whether or not an advertisement on a web site is doing its job. This is because most advertisements on the Internet are click-throughs. In a click-through advertisement, the viewer is asked to click on the advertisement for more information, or to make an on-line purchase of the product being advertised. So far—and the Internet is still a fairly new medium—click-throughs do not seem to work very well. Less than one percent of click-through advertisements are actually clicked on.

This is a problem for the companies selling advertising on the Internet. Advertisers can quickly find out whether or not their advertisements are helping them make money. This is because they can calculate each day how many viewers actually clicked on their advertisements. As a result, many advertisers who were excited about the Internet only a few years ago and were willing to spend millions of dollars on Internet advertising have since decided to spend much less, or have stopped advertising on the Internet altogether. Some of the companies that hoped to make lots of money selling Internet advertising have also become dot bombs and have gone out of business.

(continued)

Dot Com = Dot Bomb? -

Surf around the web, looking at the types of advertising that are currently being used on the Internet. Check out some of your favorite web sites. Make certain that you also check out such portals as MSN.com, Excite.com, Yahoo.com, and CNN.com.

1. In the chart below, list three products that you found advertised on the Internet. Then write how the ad tried to get you to click on it. Was that attempt a good or bad one? Why?

Product	How to get you to click	Good or bad attempt/why?

Now imagine that you are working for an advertising firm that designs Internet advertisements for companies that want to use the Internet to sell products.

2. In the chart below, list three things you would do to encourage Internet surfers to click on your advertisements. Then tell why you think your idea would work.

Encouragements	Why this would work

Because Internet advertising companies are still looking for advertising techniques that actually work, anything you come up with that is new may be an improvement over what is currently being used!

Glossary

click-through—an advertisement on the Internet that, if clicked on, takes the viewer to a web site at which the viewer can get more information about the product or make an on-line purchase of that product.

cookie—a unique identifier put on your computer by web sites when you surf the Internet. That cookie identifies you to the web site when you return to it, or to other web sites that share cookies with each other.

cool hunting—the process used by some advertisers to try to figure out what teens are and are not interested in. Cool hunters interview teens at shopping malls, on the street, and near schools and social events. They use the information they find to develop advertising campaigns aimed at teens.

data mining—the practice by advertisers in which they use demographics and psychographics gathered about consumers to make advertising decisions.

demographics—statistics about people grouped by such information as age, gender, ethnicity, geography, and income. For example, we know that the demographic group that watches the most television is women over 60 years of age.

experiential marketing—an effort in recent years by advertisers to focus on the experience that consumers have with a product rather than the product itself. For example, advertisements for men's shaving products emphasize that the products help a man feel more like a man. Similarly, an advertisement for a woman's perfume would emphasize femininity rather than the fragrance of the product.

frequency—the number of times a particular group of people is exposed to an advertisement or series of advertisements for a particular advertiser. Logically, it will cost the advertiser more to run advertisements more frequently.

hard cut—a film- or video-editing technique in which one scene or image on the screen abruptly ends and another scene or image abruptly appears. Hard cuts are increasingly common in television advertisements today, which may contain dozens of cuts in a thirty-second advertisement. This constantly shifting visual imagery is used to attract and maintain the viewer's attention.

jingle—a short song written particularly for the purpose of advertising a product on radio and television. The song will usually include the name of the product, and may also have a short, catchy description of the product or its qualities. Famous examples include Burger King's "Have it Your Way" and Coke's "It's the Real Thing."

logo—the symbol that is used to identify a particular brand. For example, McDonald's golden arches; the red, white, and blue ball of Pepsi; and the Nike swoosh. The logo can also contain a word or words, such as the distinctive way in which the word Coca-Cola appears in Coke's logo.

point-of-purchase advertising—this can include cardboard cutouts, banners, neon signs, and other advertising placed in stores, restaurants, and other places where the product is offered for sale.

portal—a web site that is often used by consumers as their start page. Such portals include Yahoo and MSN. Portals offer content that is interesting for web surfers, which helps those portals gather viewers. The portals make money by selling advertising space to advertisers who want to sell to web surfers.

product placement—when advertisers pay producers of movies and television shows to have their product used by characters in those movies or television shows. The best-known example may be the placement of Reese's Pieces in the movie *E.T.* Product placement is a form of stealth marketing.

pseudo-event—one form of stealth marketing. The prefix *pseudo*- means "fake." Pseudo-events are fake news events that are really a form of advertising. Since the news media rely on advertising to make a profit, they often willingly participate in pseudo-events. A well-known example of a pseudo-event occurred when M&Ms candy added the color blue and paid to have the Empire State Building lit up in blue to celebrate.

psychographics–people grouped by their interests, attitude, values, and habits (including buying habits).

puffery–a claim by an advertiser that sounds good but cannot be truly measured, evaluated, or compared. For example, an advertisement that tells you that a product is "the coolest thing ever."

pull marketing–marketing, including advertising, directed toward the person who will ulitmately use the product. For example, most advertisements for children's cereals are aimed at children, who will not buy the product, but will influence the buying decision. Contrast with push marketing.

push marketing–marketing, including advertising, that is directed toward the people who help a product get distributed. for example, doctors often receive advertisements for medicines that they prescribe for patients. Contrast with pull marketing.

qualitative research–research by advertisers that focuses on what types of people are exposed to an advertisement, remember an advertisement, buy the advertised product, and so on. The description of the people may be based on demographics or psychographics. Contrast with quantitative research.

quantitative research–research by advertisers that focuses on how many people are exposed to an advertisement, remember an advertisement, buy the advertised product, and so on. Contrast with qualitative research.

reach–the number of people who are exposed to an advertisement or a series of advertisements for a particular advertiser. Logically, it usually costs an increasing amount of money to reach a larger number of people.

recto–the right side page of a newspaper or magazine. Americans usually move their eyes automatically to the right side page, so that an advertisement on a recto page will usually cost the advertiser more than an advertisement on the opposite (verso) side.

stealth marketing–occurs when an advertiser engages in marketing activities but attempts to make it look like it is not. Pseudo-events and product placement are two examples of stealth marketing.

tagline–a slogan, often presented at the end of a television or radio advertisement, or at the bottom of a newspaper or magazine advertisement. Its purpose is to help make the product and the advertisement memorable to the consumer. Examples include KFC's "We do chicken right" and Nike's "Just do it."

verso–the left side page of a newspaper or magazine. Americans usually move their eyes automatically to the right side page, so that an advertisement on a verso page will usually cost the advertiser less than an advertisement on the opposite (recto) side.

Additional Resources

Publications

Fox, Roy F., *Harvesting Minds: How TV Commercials Control Kids* (Westport, CT: Praeger, 1996).

Gay, Kathlyn, *Caution! This May Be an Advertisement: A Teen Guide to Advertising* (New York: Franklin Watts, 1992).

Johnston, Carla B., *Screened Out: How the Media Control Us and What We Can Do About It* (Armonk, NY: M.E. Sharpe, 2000).

Kilbourne, Jean, *Can't Buy My Love: How Advertising Changes the Way We Think and Feel* (New York: Touchstone, 2000).

Mierau, Christina B., *Accept No Substitutes: The History of American Advertising* (Minneapolis: Lerner, 2000).

Potter, W. James, *Media Literacy,* 2nd ed. (Thousand Oaks: Sage, 2001).

Silverblatt, Art, and Ellen M. Enright Eliceiri, *Dictionary of Media Literacy* (Westport, CT: Greenwood, 1997).

Silverblatt, Art, *Media Literacy: Keys to Interpreting Media Messages* (Westport, CT: Praeger, 1995).

Sivulka, Juliann, *Soap, Sex, and Cigarettes: A Cultural History of American Advertising* (Belmont, CA: Wadsworth, 1997).

Web Sites

Adbusters
   adbusters.org/home

Alliance for a Media Literate America
   www.nmec.org

Center for Media Education
   www.cme.org

Center for Media Literacy
   www.medialit.org

Children Now: Children & the Media
   www.childrennow.org/media

Finding What You Need on the Web
   www.thirteen.org/edonline/primer/jungle.html

Just Think
   www.justthink.org

Media Awareness Network
   www.media-awareness.ca

Media Literacy Clearinghouse
   www.med.sc.edu:1081

Media Literacy Online Project
   interact.uoregon.edu/MediaLit/HomePage

PBS's "The Merchants of Cool"
   www.pbs.org/wgbh/pages/frontline/shows/cool

Propaganda Analysis
   carmen.artsci.washington.edu/propaganda

SmartGirl
   www.smartgirl.org

Share Your Bright Ideas

We want to hear from you!

Your name_____Date_____

School name_____

School address_____

City _____State _____Zip_____Phone number (_____)_____

Grade level(s) taught_____Subject area(s) taught_____

Where did you purchase this publication?_____

In what month do you purchase a majority of your supplements?_____

What moneys were used to purchase this product?

_____School supplemental budget   _____Federal/state funding   _____Personal

Please "grade" this Walch publication in the following areas:

	A	B	C	D
Quality of service you received when purchasing	A	B	C	D
Ease of use	A	B	C	D
Quality of content	A	B	C	D
Page layout	A	B	C	D
Organization of material	A	B	C	D
Suitability for grade level	A	B	C	D
Instructional value	A	B	C	D

COMMENTS:_____

_____

What specific supplemental materials would help you meet your current—or future—instructional needs?

_____

Have you used other Walch publications? If so, which ones?_____

May we use your comments in upcoming communications?   _____Yes   _____No

Please **FAX** this completed form to **888-991-5755**, or mail it to

Customer Service, Walch Publishing, P. O. Box 658, Portland, ME 04104-0658

We will send you a **FREE GIFT** in appreciation of your feedback. **THANK YOU!**